THE AUDUBON
NATURE
ENCYCLOPEDIA

THE AUDUBON NATURE ENCYCLOPEDIA

SPONSORED BY THE NATIONAL AUDUBON SOCIETY

VOLUME 2

BI - CA

CURTIS BOOKS
A division of
The Curtis Publishing Company
Philadelphia — New York

CREATED AND PRODUCED BY
COPYLAB PUBLISHING COUNSEL, INC., NEW YORK

Copyright © 1964, 1965
by
National Audubon Society, Inc.

First Printing

All rights reserved. No part of the text or illustrations in this book may be used without the written permission of the copyright owner. Library of Congress Card Catalog Number 64-8877.

Published simultaneously in Canada by
Curtis Distributing Company, Ltd., Toronto.

Printed in the United States of America

PICTORIAL ACKNOWLEDGMENTS, Volume 2

Allan D. Cruickshank*, VIII, 197, 210 top, 220, 245 top, 250, 255, 261, 263, 276, 284, 303 top, 324, 368, 382 —Brodrick (National Park Service), 193 —Hans J. Peeters, 195, 196 —Michael H. Bevans, 199, 317 —Maud H. Purdy, 200, 201 —Louis Agassiz Fuertes, 203 —Monroe Carrington*, 205 top —Allan Brooks, 205, 206 top right, bottom left, bottom right, 207 all except bottom left, 208 top left, bottom left and center, 218, 267, 277, 278, 329, 331, 333, 366 —Thase Daniel*, 206 top left —Roger Tory Peterson, 206 top center, bottom center, 208 top center, bottom right, 246-247, 248-249, 256, 257, 275, 285, 293, 327, 328, 359, 361 —Walter Webber, 207 bottom left —George M. Sutton, 208 top right —Robert P. Allen, 210 bottom —Charles and Elizabeth Schwartz, 211 bottom —John H. Gerard*, 212 top left, 332, 381 —John K. Terres, 212 top right, 213 bottom, 244 top left —Hugo Schroder*, 213 top —G. Ronald Austing*, 217 top 2, 227 top 3, 323 —Donald Koehler* and G. Ronald Austing*, 217 bottom center —Jerome Wexler*, 217 bottom —John H. Storer, 222, 223, 230, 231 —Lynwood Chace*, 227 bottom, 344 —Sonja Bullaty*, 229 —Carl Koford*, 235 —Walter Ferguson, 237 —H.A. Thornhill*, 243 —Buck Reeves*, 244 top right, 365 —Leonard Lee Rue III*, 244 bottom —Barbara Nisbett*, 245 bottom —Roland C. Clement, 252-253 —Gordon S. Smith*, 259 —George Porter*, 265 —R. Bruce Horsfall, 290, 292 —Herman W. Kitchen*, 273 —N.E. Beck, Jr.*, 274 —Hugh Spencer*, 282 —Lee Adams, 283, 287, 288, 334, 335, 376 —H. Wayne Trimm. 286, 301 (courtesy of the New York State Conservationist) —Edwin C. Park*, 289 —David and Sue Fables, 295, 296 —Helen Cruickshank*, 297 —Richard J. Scheich*, 299 —Clifford Matteson*, 300 —United States Fish and Wildlife Service, 303 bottom —Frank A. Tinker*, 304, 305, 306 —Billy Jones*, 307 —W.D. Berry, 310, 311, 312, 313, 375, 379 —Ed Cesar*, 315 —Ralph J. Donahue*, 318, 319, 320 —John R. Clawson*, 321 —Captain C.W.R. Knight, 330 —R. Glover*, 337 —Robert Jackowitz, 339 —Edwin Way Teale, 347, 348, 351, 388 —Art Bilsten*, 354 —Hugh M. Halliday*, 350 —Lewis Kirk, 355, 356 —H. O'Neil*, 369 —Richard C. Finke*, 373 —Charles J. Ott, 326, 371 —National Park Service, 374 —Wilford L. Miller*, 377 —R. Van Nostrand*, 380 —Roche*, 384 —United States Department of Agriculture, 386 —Robert C. Hermes*, 339 —Alpha Photo Associates, 363 —Winston Pote-Shostal, 364

*Photographs from Photo-Film Department of National Audubon Society

BIOLOGICAL CONTROL

In nature many kinds of animals live at the expense of others. The predators—for example, wolves, foxes, bobcats, weasels, hawks, eagles, and owls—prey upon smaller animals, especially the rodent millions. Thus they suppress the numbers of rodents and help keep them in check (*See Balance of Nature*).

Songbirds—The flycatchers, thrushes, wrens, warblers, and others—feed largely upon insects and thus help to suppress the insect numbers. Perhaps even more important than birds in the suppression of insects are the predatory and parasitic insects that often exploit insects that are harmful to forests or to man's agricultural crops. Climate and weather are usually most important of all in limiting the abundance of insects and of other animals.

Biologists and agriculturalists can do nothing about climate or weather, but they can help to suppress a destructive insect pest by fostering or increasing its natural enemies. When they do so, whether it is by helping to increase the population of insect-eating birds or by introducing disease organisms or parasitic enemies of pest insects, they are practicing biological control. The following story tells of some of the methods of studying and possibly increasing the natural enemies of the caterpillars of the lodgepole needle-miner, which is sometimes destructive to forests of lodgepole pine. —J.K.T.

The adult lodgepole needle-miner is a small, mottled, gray moth about a quarter of an inch long. Its caterpillars (the larval or immature form) subsist upon the needles of lodgepole pines in the forests of western North America. Whenever weather or other changing forces of nature become favorable to the lodgepole needle-miner, this usually obscure little insect can increase its numbers at an astonishing rate.

Because of such increases the lodgepole needle-miner gained notoriety during 1963. Outbreaks in the Canadian Rockies and in the Sierra Nevada of California caused striking foliage losses and discoloration to thousands of acres of lodgepole pine forests.

Entomologists have determined that it takes two full years for a single generation of the needle-miner to develop. The moths normally appear from mid-July into August of the second year. They lay their minute, yellow eggs beneath needle sheaths or bud scales, in crevices in the bark of twigs and in partially mined-out needles.

The tiny caterpillars hatch late in the summer and enter the tips of the needles, which they occupy during the ensuing winter. Growth and development are renewed with the arrival of spring. The larger caterpillars pass a second winter in their needle "mines," completing development and metamorphosis into moths by midsummer of the second year.

The needle-miner's manner of development is not common in the insect world because its two-year-long generations are discrete. Its reproductive stage, the moth, occurs only in alternate years. During its life-span, a single caterpillar may mine out and destroy five or more pine needles.

The depredations of the needle-miner alone have not caused the death of the large numbers of trees that become infected. The principal destruction of foliage occurs in the second year of each needle-miner generation. Since the miners are young and small during the first year, trees may recuperate to some degree. However, repeated and severe needle losses eventually suppress the growth of the lodgepoles and render them more vulnerable to the attacks of other insects.

It is of particular interest that needle-miners, are not normally attracted to very young or stunted lodgepole pines that are three or four feet in height. In the event that the older, taller trees succumb to this defoliator or to secondary insect enemies that might follow, the young trees usually grow up to replace their less fortunate ancestors.

Canadian outbreaks of the lodgepole needle-miner over a 10-year span were terminated when a particularly cold winter killed almost all of the caterpillars in the outbreak areas. But in California, where a milder climate prevails, outbreaks of longer duration persist.

Whether or not outbreaks of lodgepole needle-miners may be detrimental or beneficial natural processes, a majority of the officials and entomologists concerned have judged them contrary to the public interest when they occur in recreational areas of forests. As a consequence, personnel of the Southwest Pacific Forest and Range Experiment Station, United States Forest Service, and the University of California have participated in programs directed toward the control of the lodgepole needle-miner.

Research has centered on the recognition, evaluation, and manipulation of the needle-miner's native, natural enemies (parasites and predators) and the use of these enemies in limiting needle-miner populations to tolerable levels (*See under Insect: Predators and Parasites*).

The list of parasites and predators associated with the lodgepole needle-miner exceeds 40. Most of these are tiny, almost microscopic parasitic wasps. Their relationships with their foliage-consuming prey, with one another, and with the lodgepole pine forest community as a whole, are unbelievably complex.

A few of these parasitic wasps are so intimately associated with the needle-miner that they attack no other insect and are able to develop in perfect synchrony with the unusual two-year cycle of their host. These are potentially very effective insects for needle-miner control. Several of the natural enemies are opportunists that, although not attuned to the needle-miner's cycle, take advantage of this host whenever it is available to them. Certain of these can also be important control agents. Others attack the needle-miner only occasionally. There are also several enemies of needle-miner parasites and predators that, under special circumstances, may hinder the natural control of the defoliator.

Most attention has been directed toward studies of the parasitic wasps. In 1961, however, investigators became aware that they had been overlooking a very important natural enemy of the lodgepole needle-miner—the mountain chickadee. Earlier investigators had only rarely mentioned the chickadee, and then only as a possibly occasional predator. It had been generally assumed that the

A parasitic wasp searches for the larvae of the lodgepole needle-miner

mountain chickadee was a general, nonselective insect predator. Now, however, a program was started to learn how this bird would be affected by an insecticidal control program against the needle-miner in Yosemite National Park.

Toward this end, 80 nest-boxes for chickadees were placed in the forest by investigators and bird census surveys were begun in the vicinity of Tuolumne Meadows. Unfortunately, soon after nesting observations had begun (six broods had been hatched) and just prior to the application of malathion insecticide to approximately 5,000 acres, the investigators were compelled to terminate their bird studies at Tuolumne Meadows.

Although it was not possible to follow the plan for an evaluation of the effect of malathion in diesel fuel upon the chickadee, the curiosity of the investigators had been aroused when they noticed large flocks of mountain chickadees in another needle-miner outbreak in the Inyo National Forest. Upon resurveying Inyo in the fall of 1961, they were impressed by the relative abundance of chickadees in association with the insect.

This apparent concentration of birds in areas of high needle-miner density prompted the investigators to collect a few birds in order to analyze their stomach contents. Approximately 640 needle-miner caterpillars were found in the stomachs of the first ten birds. A second plan for a more extensive study of bird predation was thereupon formulated.

Working with a "weasel" snow vehicle and on snowshoes loaned by the university's Department of Physiology, the investigators laid out two study plots, each one half of a square mile. One was within the infestation while the other was separated but nearly identical in elevation (9,000 feet) and stand composition. Here attempts were made to fill in the unknown pieces of the chickadee's life history and to establish its relationships with the lodgepole needle-miner.

The plots were well-supplied with nest boxes that augmented the natural nesting sites of the mountain chickadee—primarily natural cavities in trees and old woodpecker excavations. The nest boxes were located systematically along parallel survey lines which were also used for observing bird numbers and habits.

As a result, the investigators were able to accumulate a great deal of information about the chickadee. Mountain chickadees are essentially residents in the Canadian Life Zone of the high

A biologist sets out bird nest boxes

mountains of western North America. When not nesting, they may travel in bands of 100 or more, ranging through the trees in search of insects. They are active little birds, easily approached and observed, but their quick actions made it difficult to determine their manner of feeding on the infestations of the lodgepole needle-miner.

It is an efficient method, however. The chickadee breaks with its bill the convex surface of a pine needle near the base of the part mined by the caterpillar, and strips back a narrow flap of the needle, about a quarter of an inch long. Thus, the caterpillar is exposed and quickly extracted by the chickadee. By this means, a bird may find and consume up to six needle-miners in 10 seconds.

As many as 275 caterpillars have been recovered from the stomach of a single bird. The characteristics of chickadee feeding were easily recognized and were helpful indicators in evaluating the influence of the birds on the reduction of needle-miners.

During the fall and winter of 1963 the chickadees concentrated their feeding efforts on the needle-miner in out-

Mountain chickadees feed on destructive moth larvae

break areas, and in doing so ignored practically all other available food. In technical terms, this is called a functional response to high prey density. These birds displayed important characteristics of other efficient predators that have been imported or manipulated for use in practical insect control programs in the past. The chickadees, then, may be categorized as agents of biological control.

In their studies the investigators hoped to determine whether or not chickadees would increase in numbers in the presence of abundant food and places to nest. They also hoped to find out how minimum space requirements of family groups and other limiting factors affected their rate of increase. Thus, in technical terms again, they hoped to determine whether or not the mountain chickadee would demonstrate both functional and numerical responses to high prey densities.

Birds and their food were considered in great detail by members of the United States Biological Survey in the decade and a half preceding the turn of the century and up to the 1930's. Although this work was valuable and extensive, it led, in many cases, to numerous exorbitant claims concerning the ability of birds to control insect outbreaks. As an unfortunate consequence, the role of birds in insect control became a matter of controversy.

Despite the current lapse in studies of the effects of birds feeding on insects, the mountain chickadee and other native insect-eating birds warrant our attention. Although present-day studies of their food habits suggests their value in insect control, it seems unlikely that insectivorous birds alone can stem the needle-miners at their higher levels of abundance. Yet, together with the other suppressive forces of the lodgepole pine habitat, mountain chickadees contribute to the abatement of peak populations of the lodgepole needle-miner.

Outbreaks of insects rise and fall according to variations of the natural forces that affect their procreation and survival. Within the limits imposed by local climates, different natural enemies work with varying efficiency at different levels of host abundance. All are important. These and the many other related effects within a forest community maintain a teetering balance. At times the seesaw may tip violently. Rarely, if ever, does it crash beyond recovery to one side or the other. It is unlikely, therefore, that the lodgepole needle-miner will exterminate its source of livelihood, the lodgepole pine. Nor will natural enemies exterminate this insect.

More research attention must be given to the natural regulatory and suppressive agencies of the forest environment (parasites, predators, diseases, meteorological phenomena) so that they may be effectively enlisted in man's behalf whenever possible. If insecticides are called for, it is mandatory that the biotic relationships of the organisms in the environment be understood, and how they may be affected if a poison is to be used.

Otherwise, the risk of creating unwarranted biotic imbalances that may violently and irreparably destroy our forests will remain great.

—A.D.T. and S.G.H.

BIOLOGY

The scientific study of organisms, living or extinct, is called biology. The term is a combination of two Greek words, and means the study of modes of life.

Living things are almost incredibly diverse. They possess so many attributes that these have become separate fields of studies in themselves. Because of this diversity, biology has been divided into many more or less independent sciences, each a part of man's growing knowledge of life itself.

Some of the larger fields of knowledge within the realm of biology are: botany, the science of plants; zoology, of animals; bacteriology, of bacteria;

morphology, of the structure of living things; taxonomy, of their relationship and classification; physiology, of their activities; ecology, of their interrelationships and their environments; embryology, of their development before birth; paleontology, of fossil life.

To the citizen and the amateur naturalist, the findings of ecology provide perhaps the most important lessons of biology. —G.B.S.

BIOME (*See under Life Zone*)

BIRCH

There are about 35 known species of birches in the world. For the most part, they are scattered throughout the northern hemisphere, and of all trees, the birch has the most northerly range. The birches usually grow to a normal tree size, however, a few species remain shrubs. Fifteen species are native to North America; among these are the yellow birch, the paper birch, the black birch, the river birch, and the gray birch.
—M.H.B.

Black Birch
Other Common Names—Sweet birch, cherry birch
Scientific Name—*Betula lenta*
Family—Corylaceae (hazel family)
Range—Southern Quebec, southwestern Maine to eastern Ohio, and southward to northern Georgia and Tennessee
Habitat—Although typically a highland tree, it also grows at low altitudes in the north
Leaves—May be alternate or borne in pairs; 2½ to 5 inches long, broadly lance-shaped with a gradually tapering point, and with either a right-angled or heart-shaped base, and finely toothed margins; rather shiny, turning clear yellow in autumn
Bark—Extremely variable with age. On sapling trees satiny bronze or mahogany-brown with little tan dash marks (lenticels); the bark becoming (on four

Black birch

to eight inch trunks) dark silver-gray to black with coarser lines and seams, then splitting vertically to form rows of broad, irregular plates. On largest trunks, may break up into rough elongate patches, revealing reddish tones
Flowers—Small, upright female heads and stout, hanging male catkins, often an inch or so long during winter but growing to about four inches and producing much yellow pollen
Fruit—Stout, little upright cones three-fourths of an inch long that open upon ripening but remain on the tree into winter

One outstanding characteristic of the black birch that sets it apart from all other birches is its rich mahogany-red bark. It is smooth and glossy in the younger trees or saplings, often becoming rough and scaly in the older trees. A second characteristic, a trait shared with the yellow birch, is the pleasant minty aroma of the leaves and bark. Because of this aroma it is commonly referred to as sweet birch in some areas. This pleasant scent is attributable to a valuable resin derived from the black birch known as oil of wintergreen.

The leaves resemble those of the beech but have much finer teeth on the edges. The surface has a corrugated effect produced by the raised areas between close-set veins. The leaves vary in shades from a pale lemon-yellow to an orange shade in the autumn.

The black birch is chiefly a tree of the Appalachian forest of the northeastern states and the southern uplands where in some areas it is second only to the oak in abundance. Frequently lady fern and maidenhair grow about the base of the trunk of this tree.

The wood of the black birch is regarded as one of the better, more important hardwoods. A heavy, close-grained wood, it is resistant to impact and considered as strong as mahogany and in the past was frequently sold as "mountain mahogany." Doors, windows, crates, woodenware, and furniture are among its structural uses. Wood alcohol, oil of birch, and birch beer are also produced from its wood, bark, and twigs.

During the winter the black birch can be identified by its stout, upright cones. These remain on the branches and twigs throughout the winter and are light brown in color with overlapping scales.
—M.H.B.

Gray Birch
Other Common Names—Poplar-leaved birch, poverty birch, old field birch
Scientific Name—*Betula populifolia*
Family—Corylaceae (hazel family)
Range—Nova Scotia west to Quebec, southwestern Ontario and northern Indiana; south through New England, New York, Delaware, Pennsylvania, and upland Virginia
Habitat—Often grows in clumps (from sprouts) on poor soil or in burns. It is also a pioneering, or first-growth, tree on burned-over forest land
Leaves—Small (two to three inches), roughly triangular with a squarish base and a long point, with fine-toothed edges, lustrous and tremulous
Bark—Chalky white (but not peeling as in white birch), with horizontal black lines and triangular black scars at branch junctions. Base of trunk usually rough and blackened
Flowers—Slender catkins, one to two inches long in winter, male lengthening to three or four inches in spring
Fruit—A stumpy little cone (three-fourths of an inch long) from which seeds and scales fall upon ripening

At first glance the small gray birch may be mistaken for the trembling aspen. Like the aspen, this birch grows in little groves of its own kind. These small groups are formed by several stems branching out away from each other, appearing to rise from a common root.

The leaves of the gray birch also resemble the aspen, particularly in the autumn when both take on a soft golden hue. Perhaps because of these resemblances the gray birch is also called the poplar birch or poplar-leaved birch.

The small gray birch is a short-lived

Flowering branch of the gray birch, Betula populifolia, about mid-April, with drooping staminate and erect pistillate catkins, the latter having recently emerged from a winter bud.

BIRCH 201

Staminate catkins in winter condition, winter buds and twigs, fruit spurs, bracts, nutlets, and leaves of each species. Only leaves shown in 5a, 6a, 6b.

1. *Sweet birch*, Betula lenta
2. *Yellow birch*, Betula lutea
3. *River birch*, Betula nigra
4. *Gray birch*, Betula populifolia
5. *Paper birch*, Betula papyrifera
5a. *Paper birch*, Betula papyrifera, *var.* cordifolia
6. *European weeping birch*, Betula pendula; *showing two types of leaves*
6a. *European weeping cutleaf birch*, Betula pendula, *var.* dalecarlica
6b. *European weeping cutleaf birch*, Betula pendula, *var.* gracilis
7. *European white birch* Betula pendula

tree. By the time the saplings, growing in a circular formation around the larger birch, have reached their maturity, the parent tree had died or is dying. The mature gray birch seldom exceeds 25 to 30 feet in height, with a trunk diameter of five to eight inches. The surrounding forest often so shades them that they are unable to produce further new growth. The trees then die, and the seeds that have taken root in more favorable areas are left to carry on the species.

Dead gray birches are characterized by banks of stiff, cup-shaped fungi growing along the trunks. These cause the trees to rot and become so weak that a slight tug will bring them to the ground. Once on the ground the trunks are soon reduced to soil again; all that is left of the birches are sections of their bark. This life sequence is representative of a good many trees that do not form part of the tall, overshadowing climax forest.

Another name, poverty birch, seems a more apt description of this small birch as it grows on the poor soil of fire-ravaged fields, lands worn out by excessive cultivation, roadsides, and the damp, clay soils of some woods. In reclaiming these areas it helps the deforested and abused lands, after which it gives way to the larger species.

—M.H.B.

Paper Birch
Other Common Names—Canoe birch, white birch
Scientific Name—*Betula papyrifera*
Family—Corylaceae (hazel family)
Range—Woods, especially on slopes, in Labrador and Newfoundland west to

Alaska, south to Nova Scotia, New England, New York, northern New Jersey, uplands of Pennsylvania and West Virginia; west through northern Ohio, northern Indiana, northern Illinois to Iowa and Minnesota

Habitat—Often colonizes damp areas after fires have destroyed other vegetation

Leaves—Broadly lance-shaped (base rounded or heart-shaped), two to three inches long, not shiny

Bark—White or creamy, sometimes tan or smokey, but always peeling naturally into papery layers. Twigs, reddish-brown

Flowers—Like gray birch, but unlike other birches

Fruit—The fruiting heads are cylindrical and pendant, and the scales of the "cone" are quickly shed at maturity

This species is generally taller, straighter, and stouter than the gray birch, with heights of 80 feet and trunk diameters to 3 feet. It is also more a tree of the deep forest and more often used for lumber than the gray birch. The paper birch grows singly and, though it sometimes stands like the aspen, is seldom found in small leaning groups. The chalky bark peels up on its curls showing tones of buff, pinkish- or yellow-brown underneath as it is stripped off. Occasionally the bark has a smoky color and the twigs are reddish rather than black as in the gray birch.

A handsome tree, the paper birch is more durable and stronger than the gray birch. However, both species, particularly the slender gray birch, are noted for their ability to bend to the ground under the weight of ice and snow, then return to their normal positions, apparently none the worse for the wear.

In earlier times the paper birch, sometimes referred to as the canoe birch, was used by the American Indians and early settlers to make their slim crafts. The Indians would strip the bark, which can be peeled off in broad sheets, from the birch, stretch it, and then lace it onto a frame. The joinings and small knotholes were closed with pitch, usually the resin of the pine or balsam. The bark also served as a covering for Indian tepees and the birch wood was used for the snowshoe frames. —M.H.B.

BIRD

Birds are by all odds, next to man himself, one of nature's most interesting creations. Fortunately, also, they are becoming more and more widely appreciated by man. Why this is so is uncertain; perhaps it is because birds sing and dance much as people do when they are happy, and this may attract man toward them. Their lives are simpler than is man's, however, since they solve most of their problems by instinct. Perhaps we envy them this a little, since thinking out problems in a logical fashion is sometimes very difficult.

In any event, getting to know birds is an enriching experience; it helps satisfy our need to feel at home amidst nature on this planet. So few of us live next to the soil today that we need to recover our contacts with the ageless realities of nature. Somehow, although man feels outside nature today, he realizes that he is still part of nature and must understand her to understand himself. Birds help provide that essential contact and give man many insights that help strengthen him. —R.C.C.

Archaeopteryx, the oldest known bird

Ruby-throated hummingbirds

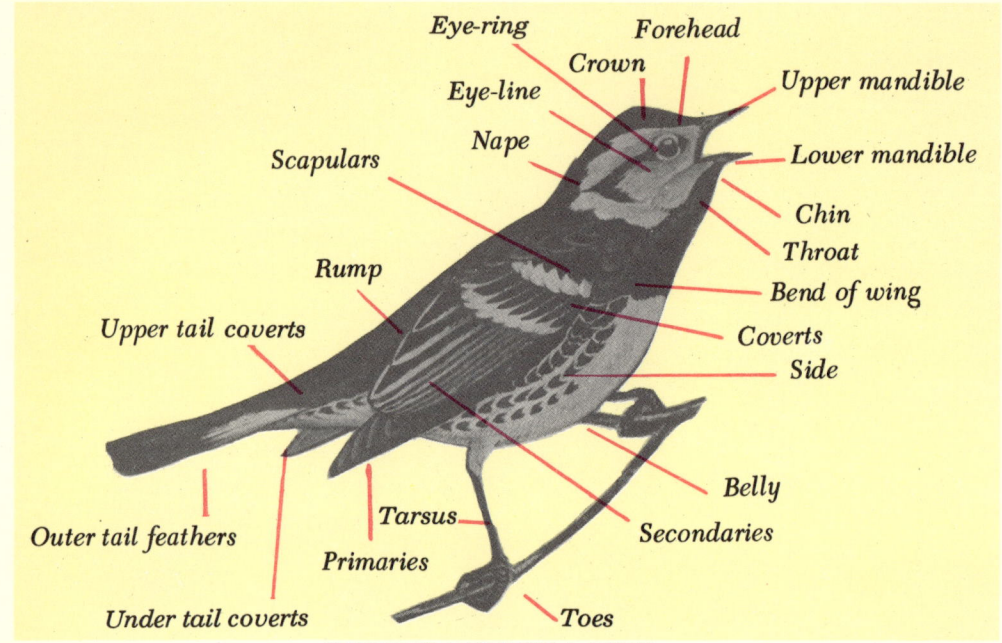

TOPOGRAPHY OF A BIRD

What is a Bird?

Birds belong to the class Aves, and are vertebrate animals. However, of all animals, only birds have the body covered with feathers. Feathers are extremely efficient in heat insulating and in waterproofing a bird's body. They also afford an immediate basis for determining the animal class to which its possessors belong.

Evolution of Birds

All of the animals with backbones have a common ancestry in fishlike amphibians that crawled up and out of the water in the Paleozoic Era, about 300 million years ago. Some of the descendants of these first amphibians developed characteristics that placed them in a more advanced class—that of the reptiles. Some of these, in turn, diverged from the ancestral stock, under evolutionary pressures; some assumed a bipedal gait, while others kept all four feet on the ground. One group of small, four-footed reptiles, quite inconspicuous in an age of lumbering giants, evolved into warm-blooded, hair-covered creatures. These were the first mammals, and their advent has been placed at about 190 million years ago, in the Triassic Period. Another reptile group, one of those that had learned to walk on the hind legs, also developed an internal heating system, but instead of a coat of hair, this group had long, frayed reptilian scales that gradually modified into feathers. These were the first birds, and traces of them have been found as far back as the Jurassic Period, 130 million years ago. Skeletal and other internal evidence indicate that the closest living kin to the birds are the crocodilians; man himself is more closely allied to the platypus of Australia than he is to the birds.

Modern birds demonstrate their reptilian origin in a number of ways. There is no significant difference in the internal anotomy, except perhaps in the heart. Feathers are highly evolved scales, and the feet of birds are still scale-covered. The young of birds and of many reptiles are hatched from eggs, rather than born alive as are most mammals.

BIRD 205

From top—primary feathers of osprey, Laysan albatross, and snowy owl

Orders, Families, and Species

A multitude of species, and perhaps as many as six whole orders of birds, have become extinct and are known only from fossil evidence. Today, the professional ornithologists generally recognize 27 or 29 orders of living birds, divided among 154 to 170 families that contain a total of about 8,600 species. Minor variations within the species increase the figure to nearly 30,000 recognizable forms of species and subspecies.

North America has 74 families and 736 species arranged in 20 orders. These orders are those of the loons, the grebes, the albatrosses and petrels, the pelicans and gannets, the herons and their allies, the geese and ducks, the day-flying birds of prey, the relatives of domestic fowl (turkeys, quail, and grouse), the cranes and rails, the shorebirds and gulls, the pigeons, the parrots, the cuckoos, the owls, the goatsuckers, the swifts and hummingbirds, the trogons, the kingfishers, the woodpeckers, and the very large order of the passerines, which includes flycatchers, swallows, thrushes, warblers, blackbirds, finches, and many other so-called songbirds.

I— Loon

II— Grebe

206 BIRD

III — Petrel

IV — Pelican

V — Heron

IX — Rail

X — Gull

XI — Dove

BIRD 207

VI — Duck

VII — Vulture

VIII — Pheasant

XII — Parrot

XIII — Cuckoo

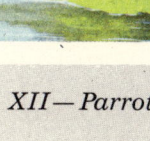
XIV — Owl

208 BIRD

XV—Nighthawk

XVI—Hummingbird

XVII—Trogon

XVIII—Kingfisher

XIX—Woodpecker

XX—Perching bird

Flight

The anatomy of the bird shows many adaptations for flight. One of the principal ones is the lightness of the skeleton, with the disappearance of any bone not needed in flying, with the presence of air sacs in the long bones of the body, and with a reduction of mass in the bones of the skull. The enormously enlarged breastbone has become a keel to which the flight muscles are attached. The fusion of the bones of the pelvic girdle and the vertebrae of the back, together with the strong bracing of the ribs, results in a light but rigid cage for the internal organs and a firm foundation for the beating wings. The digestive system is very efficient, producing only a small amount of waste material that is discharged almost immediately. The contour feathers are all aligned with the axis of the bird, pointing away from the head, and minimizing air drag (*See under Bird: Bird Flight*).

In addition to the general adaptations that are shared by most birds, each family has its own adaptive pattern. Some of these characteristics may be held in common with other groups, such as webbed feet among swimming birds, the thin wing and large sail area of the maritime soaring species, or the long legs of the waders. Other adaptations are peculiar to one family, and may permit it to exploit a food resource or a habitat for which other birds are not equipped, or not well fitted. The spatulate bill of the roseate spoonbill gives it access to the rich life of the upper inch or so of the mud flat, the spiny tail of the chimney swift allows it to nest inside hollow trees and smokestacks, and the long toes of the gallinules enable them to walk on the leaves of water lilies.

Senses

It is through the senses that animals interpret the world around them. Dogs depend largely upon scent, moles upon tactile impressions; birds, like man, live in a world of sight and sound. Only the weak-visioned New Zealand kiwi, among birds, is known to hunt by smell.

The avian eye is, in almost every species, extremely keen, and is much larger in proportion to body size than in man. Species such as the woodcock, with the eyes at the side of the head, have a 360° field of vision, most of it monocular. At the other extreme, owls have a restricted range ahead of them, all of it binocular, their eyes being set facing forward.

Hearing, among birds, is quite well developed. Man has a greater auditory range, especially so in the lower frequencies. Many species of birds apparently cannot detect high-pitched sounds that humans can hear, but some birdsongs ascend higher than our ears can discern.

Food Habits

The reptilian ancestors of birds were, in all probability, omnivorous, and so, to a varying extent, are most of their descendants. The great majority of birds feed on insects; some species eat nothing else, and comparatively few species are known that do not eat them at some time.

Most grain-feeders bring up the young on an insect diet by gradually introducing the less digestible grain as the nestlings mature. Many of the insect-eaters, such as the warblers, will take some berries and fruit. In general, though, each species with an obviously specialized bill feeds predominantly on one type of food. Only the raptorial birds can eat flesh, and this is the major item of their diet.

Only the finches and a few others have bills that are sufficiently sturdy to crack the hulls of many kinds of seeds. Only the parrots have bills that are powerful enough to break through the heavy shell of the Brazil nut. The slim, sharp-pointed warbler bill is an admirable instrument for taking small insects. The flamingos and the spoonbills are filter-

The bill of roseate spoonbills is adapted to sift and filter their food

feeders and each family has an efficient bill of a different type.

The species of landbirds that are omnivorous (those that eat vegetable matter and flesh, including insects, nestlings, and carrion) have unspecialized bills. That of the crow is a good example. The upper mandible is bridged and curving, which means that it has strength to crush the bones of small vertebrates or to tear open the tassel of an ear of corn. The straight, sharp lines mean that the bird can use the tip selectively to pick up a small seed or to puncture an egg. Blackbirds and starlings are also omnivorous, although they rely less on animal flesh. Species, such as the thrushes and the tanagers, that take fruit and berries as well as insects have similar but shorter and less powerful bills than the crow.

Courtship

The courtship patterns that precede pair-formation and mating among birds vary greatly among the different species. Male flamingos march in a dense, head-flicking mob, trumpeting excitedly, with individuals breaking away to find receptive females. Woodpeckers drum to attract mates, and ruffed grouse create a roaring vibration with rapidly beating wings. Some of the grebes use wings and feet to propel themselves along on the surface of the water; male and female move along together, caressing and gabbling all the while. Other courtship patterns are equally spectacular. Most of the smaller species limit themselves to display and song. Whatever the ritual of the species may be, its purpose is

Whooping crane courtship dance

the same: to attract and to stimulate a member of the opposite sex.

Territorial Behavior

Among the more common landbirds, song, territory, and mating are closely linked. In most species, the male returns first in the spring migration. He sets about locating a territory that satisfies the requirements of living — food, cover, and nesting sites. Song at this stage serves to notify other males that

A male robin oversees his territory

the territory is taken, and to advertise to females that a vacancy exists and that applications are being considered. As the females come through the area, the song of the male attracts, and an interested female will look over both the male and his territory. If both suit her, the pair then commences the routine of building a nest, in which they will rear the young. Other males tend to respect the warning implied in the song of the homesteader, and usually permit him to chase them back over the boundary when they have trespassed.

Length of Pair-bond

A number of sexual patterns exist among birds. Some of the larger species are believed to mate for life, or at least for the life of either partner. Eagles, geese, and most parrots are in this group. Others, such as crows and seabirds, usually take the same mate for more than one season. Ducks and the smaller landbirds stay together for the whole breeding season but seldom mate again the following year. House wrens are one of the species that often change partners with each brood; thus these wrens may have four mates in one summer.

Not all species form pairs, however. The males of the pheasants and some of the blackbirds establish harems. In a few species it is the female that has more than one mate; this occurs at times among cuckoos and cowbirds, and probably among phalaropes. Little blue herons, boat-tailed grackles, and sharp-tailed sparrows appear to be completely promiscuous.

Parental Care of Young

The amount of parental care given by the male also varies with the species. Male boat-tailed grackles never visit the nest of any of the females with which they may have mated. Among jays and some of the finches (like the rose-breasted grosbeak), the male brings food to the sitting female. With the gulls and terns, the male assumes a full

A newly hatched prairie chicken

212 BIRD

A female orchard oriole feeds her young

share of the incubation. The female phalarope abandons the nest once the eggs are laid, and the male must incubate them and then tend the young.

Some birds hatch from the egg with open eyes, well-developed legs, and a coat of feathers. These chicks are called precocial. Some examples are the chickenlike birds, the ducks and geese, and most of the shorebirds. Those chicks that are born blind, nearly naked, and helpless are called altricial. Among those with altricial young are the common songbirds, members of a large group of birds known as passerines. Altricial nestlings may take up to two weeks to develop sufficiently to leave the nest. Among some nonpasserines, the time may be even longer. Chimney swifts do not leave home until a month old, and penguins take several months before they can go off on their own.

The life expectancy of most wild birds is not great. The first year is the most hazardous; perhaps less than 20 percent of songbirds survive of the first-year generation. Each year between 40 and 60 percent of the entire adult population perishes, and a four-year-old bird would be exceptional. Captive birds, those removed from all normal wildlife hazards, often live for 20 years or more. Larger birds, such as hawks and gulls, have existed in cages for 50 years. (*See also Adaptations of Birds*) —G.B.S.

Attracting Birds by Sounds

For more than a half-century ornithologists have utilized birds' curiosity about noises to lure them into view for observation. The sound these birdwatchers have used has come to be known as the *squeak*. This *squeaking* sound can be made by the hand kissing method or by a mechanical device

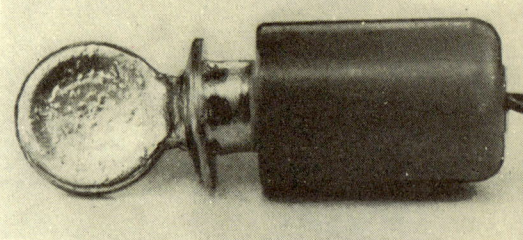

A mechanical squeaker

called a *squeaker*. Techniques vary in the hand-squeaking method, but the sound is usually produced by kissing the back of the hand, or by placing one or two fingers against the lips and sucking air in. Tone and pitch can be varied by experimentation.

Besides the hand-squeaking noises, one can simply make a *pishing* sound with the lips by expelling breath rather than inhaling. This is also found to be effective.

The squeak has resulted in some of the most interesting and important observations, affording first views of some of the rarest, or at least little-known, birds of the country. In one instance the squeak revealed a rare Bachman's warbler which, though it could be heard singing plainly, was invisible amid the dense foliage of a Carolina cypress swamp. Suddenly, the squeak brought it out of its leafy retreat to an open perch not eight feet away from the observer. On other occasions Colima warblers in the Chisos Mountains of the Texas Big Bend and painted redstarts in the high pines of western New Mexico have appeared from nowhere at the sound of a squeak.

The squeak has brought birds out of rhododendron thickets in the eastern Blue Ridge, the California Sierra, the Arizona desert, and the spruce forests of Maine. It has attracted migrants from the dense mangroves of Bush Key, Dry Tortugas, and the "hammocks" of the Kissimmee Prairie and the Everglades. It has brought up seaside sparrows on Merritt's Island, Florida, a stretch of land that moments before appeared utterly devoid of avian life.

Squeaking usually gets a response, but the responder might not wear feathers. About the last thing one would expect to respond is a snake, yet on occasion this has been what has appeared. And one time on a Texas ranch, while a group of students from the Audubon Camp were trying to squeak up a Texas jay, a gray fox appeared staring curiously in response to the squeak. The sounding of the squeak has also caused excited fox squirrels to come rushing to investigate the noise.

Once in the North Carolina mountains, a wildcat came sneaking, belly to the ground at the sound of the high-pitched squeak. Raccoons, with their sharp-visaged, black-masked faces screwed into expectant curiosity, as well as gray squirrels of the West, have also often answered the call of the squeak.

Great-horned, barred, and screech owls have swept overhead, and Cooper's and sharp-shinned hawks have executed aerial somersaults when they found the squeak was not a mouse after all.

Kissing the back of one's hand is a popular method of attracting birds

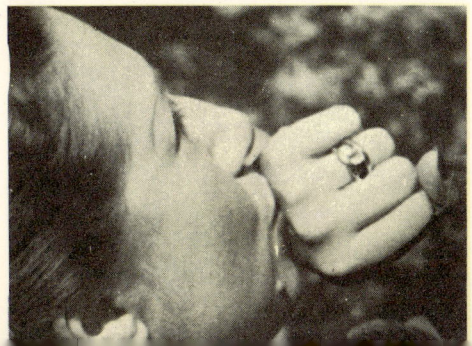

The catbird is readily attracted by a mechanical squeaker

The titmouse-chickadee combination is usually the most responsive group, often bringing others with it. The sparrows and the buntings are also highly responsive, particularly the marsh species of the sparrow. A barren reach of marsh often comes alive with sharp-tailed and seaside sparrows popping up here and there on the swaying stems, all in a high state of excitement at the sound of the squeak. The thrushes are susceptible to a degree, and mockingbirds and catbirds become all but frantic upon hearing the squeak. Blackbirds, too, will surprise the squeaker. And flocks of feeding cowbirds in an open pasture have come swarming about in an instant response.

Yet, at times, the squeak is completely unproductive. It cannot be stated that any one season of the year is better than another. There is no rule that governs the response. The best time would seem to be when young birds are in the nest and are being fed, yet it does not consistently work this way.

Some observers maintain that an imitation of the screech owl's tremulous call will attract these birds to the imitator. Imitation works remarkably well with small birds such as kinglets, warblers, and vireos; but since the imitation is difficult for some to master, the squeak often proves more productive.

"Squeaking" birds has been a source of pleasure and observational profit. It holds much promise for the birdwatcher who might not ordinarily see certain birds if he did not use the squeak.

—A.S., Jr.

Birdbanding

The banding of birds, birdbanding or *ringing* as it is called in England, involves the placing of numbered aluminum bands on the legs of birds so that these individuals later may be identified.

The information gained from birdbanding contributes to our understanding of migration—its speed, directions, and extent—and to the vital statistics of bird populations—longevity, population turnover, etc. It is a highly important method of scientific investigation.

Banding is permitted only under license from the United States Fish and Wildlife Service in Washington, D.C., or in Canada by the Canadian Wildlife Service, Ottawa. Only those at least 18 years old, who are seriously interested in birds and who can be expected to contribute to research projects under way are granted a license to take and band birds. The bands are furnished by the United States Fish and Wildlife Service in various sizes to fit hundreds of species that might be live-trapped in wire cages baited with food and water, or in mistnets strung between shrubs or trees along the flightways of birds. The birdbander is required to keep complete information as to the place and date of banding of each bird, its sex, age, species, and so on. This information is forwarded to the Bird Banding Office of the Patuxent Wildlife Research Center, in Laurel, Maryland, where it is processed and filed.

Everyone can contribute to the research effort based on birdbanding. All dead birds, whether shot by hunters or found dead of natural causes, should be examined for bands. If one is found it should be removed, flattened, and sent to the Bird Banding Office together with information about the location and date of discovery. The United States Fish and Wildlife Service will then inform those who return bands concerning the original banding of the bird whose identification they have returned. —R.C.C.

Several generations of American ornithologists have scientifically recorded and described most American birds. The birds' ranges are now well known, and much information is available as to their migrations, nesting habits, courtship, and other facts of their life history. Unless the birdwatcher of today is interested in revising the work of others or in filling in with the life history data that is still lacking about certain birds, he will of necessity seek to explore other unknown things about birds.

A most promising field is one that should particularly appeal to all those who have a backyard bird-feeding station and a desire to be on more intimate terms with those birds that make themselves at home there. It is knowledge about birds' everyday activities—where they spend the night, when they get up in the morning, how often they eat, drink, sing, sun themselves—that is especially lacking for many species. Once a thorough study has been made of the common birds, then one is in a position to ask why they act the way they do.

Already much has been accomplished. Individual species have been studied with great thoroughness. For example, the song sparrow has received much detailed attention from Margaret M. Nice, a Chicago ornithologist. Birdbanders, particularly, have added to the knowledge of both the migrations of birds and the less spectacular daily movements. They have recorded an impressive array of information as to the longevity of birds. In the domestic relationships of birds birdbanders have discovered such things as matings between parent and child or between brother and sister.

This is the sort of research that does not necessitate a knowledge of bird taxonomy or laboratory techniques. There is no need for collecting birds or making long expeditions. Binocular, pencil, and notebook are the main tools required. These will probably have to be supplemented with banding equipment, and for some bird studies photography is of great value. But most important is careful observation and attention to detail. The housewife who has a feeding station under observation while washing dishes, the businessman who manages to band a few birds before leaving for work in the morning and again after returning late in the afternoon—these are the sort of people who make worthwhile contributions.

Perhaps the most imposing difficulty is that of getting started. Many people hesitate because they feel that scientific research is a bit awesome. Nothing could be further from the truth. Audubon and many of those whose names are associated with achievements in ornithology were self-taught.

Still remaining is the question of a suitable problem for study. A person may visualize himself as solving a question that has stumped ornithologists for decades. But when he begins to think of all the effort this will involve he becomes discouraged and decides that the advancement of science is not for him.

To avoid failure or discouragement, one should not begin with too ambitious a project. As simple a bird problem as possible should be found. In time this will lead to bigger things, and one will be better equipped then to make a successful go of it. As a starter one might list the different bird species that visit a feeding station and note the exact time of their arrival in the morning and time of departure later in the day. This would provide an introduction to the daily routine of local birds, and one would soon be able to group them as "early feeders," "late feeders," "regular visitors," and "sporadic visitors."

Some observers have noted that the very earliest visitor of the day is the common crow, a bird that is usually seen at the feeding station before breakfast. Two other early feeders are the mourning dove and the ruffed grouse. Mourning doves continue to come at intervals through the day while the ruffed grouse is seldom seen again until dusk. The sparrows are the most constant visitors. Chipping, field, song, tree, and white-throated sparrows often continue feeding until it is almost dark. Cardinals are in the habit of making a final visit before they settle down for the night; then it is often so dark that they can barely be distinguished on the feeder.

Few if any observers have mapped the daily routine of the evening grosbeak. For feeding station operators this is the "morning grosbeak," because it is seldom seen at feeders except in the morning. Lee Whittles, a birdbander of Glastonbury, Connecticut, has seen them feeding while it was still dark in the morning. He noted that they invariably left by noon and that they had been seen on several occasions roosting in maples late in the day.

It is not a fast rule, however, that evening grosbeaks always remain away from the feeding station during the afternoon. Particularly during the spring, when they may be getting ready for their return journey to northern nesting grounds, they are apt to make afternoon visits.

Those species that have communal habits are likely to be the ones to make early departures. Thus starlings, house sparrows, grackles, and redwings, as a rule, leave long before dusk. Goldfinches and chickadees are also among those that leave the feeding tray well before dark, but it is not known whether these species roost in their own special precincts.

Interestingly enough, both chickadees and juncos, and to a lesser extent certain other birds that visit the feeders, follow the same line of travel through the woods to an open field, which they cross by flitting from one lone tree to another. Then they cross a dirt road always at approximately the same point, and fly on through another stretch of woods to the feeding stations. They follow this route at all times of the day so that the feeders are never overly congested. While some of them are at the feeding station, others are traveling along the route or finding food at other points, perhaps along a stone wall or at the edge of the field.

To estimate the number of birds present at feeders during the winter merely by counting the number seen at any one time would be to greatly underestimate the total number. For instance, 271 goldfinches were banded one winter, and these probably represented only about half the number coming to the feeders. Yet if the number present was estimated solely by counting those feeding at the trays at any one time it would have been a total of around 25 or 30.

After listing the sequence of arrival and departure of birds at the feeding station, one can go on to locating roosting sites, following birds in their daily movements, and banding birds to determine their numbers. The problem of getting started will no longer exist. Instead the problem will now be to find time to explore the fascinating avenues of bird study that are opening up.

At this point it might be well to suggest the importance of obtaining a bird-banding permit, for if studies are to be carried out in the way suggested, banding becomes almost indispensable. To anyone who has a serious purpose in mind and intends to band birds over a period of many years, the United States Fish and Wildlife Service will extend cordial cooperation. Obtaining a permit is somewhat difficult because the government does not grant permits to persons who might quickly lose interest, and they want to be sure that all banding is done by competent and reliable persons. Application blanks are obtainable in the United States from the Bird-Banding Office, Patuxent Research Refuge, Laurel, Maryland; and in Canada from the Chief, Dominion Wildlife Service, Ottawa, Ontario.

It should be emphasized that banding songbirds does not result in many spectacular recoveries of banded birds. Birds one has banded may turn up occasionally at the station of a fellow bander 15 or 20 miles away, but the chances of any appreciable number being recorded in distant states or foreign countries is remote indeed. It would not be advisable for anyone to go into banding songbirds if this were his sole objective.

Just as interesting is the banding of birds to solve local problems. The individualizing of birds through colored bands is of the greatest assistance. Also in the sort of problem suggested—that of tracing the routes and degree of wandering among wintering birds—banding is most necessary. Of 120 banded chickadees frequenting a home station in Sharon, Massachusetts, during the winter of 1947—48, only about a dozen strayed as far as the nearest substation, and none visited substations a mile or more away. Tree sparrows were much more given to wandering. One was banded at a nearby substation on January 12. On January 26 it was taken at the main station and the next day it was back at the substation again.

Banding has shown that tree spar-

Netting of a hummingbird

rows as well as many other birds tend to return to the same wintering territory year after year, and often with the same partners. Two tree sparrows banded on the same date in the spring of 1943 at Moose Hill, Massachusetts, continued to return seasonally. They were last taken together on February 11, 1949.

Not only does banding supply one with a wealth of factual information about birds, but it may lead to unexpected lines of research. The bander has the privilege of getting on more intimate terms with birds than does a person who watches birds from a distance. To hold a living bird in one's hand is an illuminating experience. To see the minute details of feathering and to behold the intense vibrant quality of a living bird—its rapidly beating heart and sparkling eyes—is to have a better conception of a bird as a living organism.

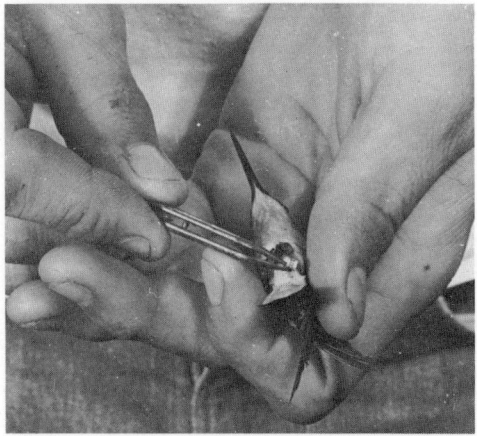
Banding in progress

The birdbander—in addition to recording seasonal movements of birds, their ages, weights, and other routines of their lives—may feel a strong challenge to know even more about the small bright-eyed creature that momentarily lies quietly in the palm of his hand and when released, springs into the air to resume its chirping or singing. What motivates a bird as it goes about its business of finding food, finding a mate, and raising its young? Is a bird actuated by the same emotions that grip humans —fear, anger, jealousy, joy, and grief— or is its life governed by instincts unrelated to human emotions?

This is much too big a problem for most observers to consider, but there are parts of it to which a person can apply himself. For example, while trapping birds for banding one can observe their ability or lack of ability to act intelligently. Some birds show an exceptional facility for finding their way in and out of ground banding traps designed to confuse the bird through labyrinthian entrances. The bird, lured into the trap by the sight of food inside, follows a complicated passageway

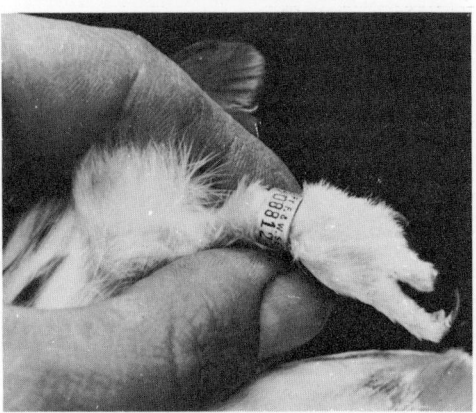
Bird banded with Fish and Wildlife Service number

A banded bird prior to release

to reach it. Once having eaten, the bird is at a loss, or so the theory is, to find its way out again.

Early in the fall of one year a birdbander was able to trap and band about 50 juncos. As the season progressed the juncos became so adept at escaping from the traps that banding fell off sharply. Only by covering the traps with burlap so that the birds within could not see the birdbander coming and then by quickly plugging the entrances with snow or pieces of cloth was he able to outwit them.

Although essentially ground-feeding birds, juncos learn to eat from vertical surfaces, perhaps through observing chickadees, nuthatches, and woodpeckers that ordinarily feed while clinging to a vertical surface. Even peanut butter sticks hanging from tree limbs and vertical woodpecker banding traps baited with suet and placed on tree trunks are not too difficult for certain juncos to learn to feed upon. Goldfinches, pine siskins, blue jays, catbirds, Baltimore orioles, and occasional tree sparrows, also mastered the vertical peanut butter sticks, but not the woodpecker trap.

Tufted titmice have shown unusual ability to master intricate devices. One investigator reported that she could not befuddle birds in banding traps by running toward them. "Approaching danger seems only to stimulate their keenness and composure," she wrote. "Their ability to find both entrance and exit without hesitation or search is apparently due to accuracy of memory."

Are juncos and tufted titmice more intelligent than other birds or did they accidentally hit upon the proper method of getting in and out of banding traps? Or has it been a gradual process, taking months or several years of experience through trial and error or through imitation of a few successful individuals? Along with birdbanding, experiments might be made that would shed much light on such questions. The ability of birds to find their way in and

A tufted titmouse

out of fairly simple traps could be tested. With birds individualized through colored bands, one could learn whether certain birds consistently showed superior intelligence and whether or not others profited by their example.

To continue with the experiment one might next test the ability of birds to find their way into or out of increasingly complex types of traps or feeding devices. Animal intelligence may be defined as the degree to which an animal is capable of modifying its behavior to cope with an emergency or to solve a problem. Thus one would have a basis for measuring intelligence by observing the success of individuals or species in mastering feeding devices. However, the researcher must guard against jumping to conclusions. Deductions can be valid only after all other possibilities have been ruled out. Thus experiments must be repeated again and again, and all other alternatives thoroughly explored. And so that others can repeat the experiments, one must thoroughly describe the methods and use devices that can be duplicated by other researchers.

Whatever subject for research has

been chosen, one should always bear in mind the obligation to present the findings to the public some day. This can be done by preparing an account of one's research in a manuscript that can be submitted to the editor of a scientific magazine. —J.V.D.

Recommended Reading

Audubon Field Notes. National Audubon Society, New York.
The Auk. Official publication, The American Ornithologists' Union.
Bird-Banding. Continuation of the *Bulletin of the Northeastern Bird-Banding Association*, (Check address in your local library.).
Bird Display and Behaviour— Edward A. Armstrong, Oxford University Press.
The Birds of America, 1840–1844— John James Audubon.
The Birds of Massachusetts and Other New England States— Edward Howe Forbush.
Check List of North American Birds— American Ornithologists' Union.
The Condor. Official publication, The Cooper Ornithological Society.
The Cowbirds: A Study in the Biology of Social Parasitism— Herbert Friedman.
A Guide to Bird Watching— Joseph J. Hickey. Oxford University Press, New York.
Life Histories of North American Birds— A. C. Bent.
Modern Bird Study— Ludlow Griscom.
Territory in Bird Life— H. Eliot Howard. London.

Bird Flight
How Birds Fly

Flying, together with hunting and homemaking, ranks among the earliest recorded interests of man. Many an early experimenter lost his life in attempting to imitate the birds.

Some of these would-be fliers or gliders were able to leave the ground, but none was able to stay aloft. One essential always lacking was the ability to maintain balance in the air. Yet every soaring bird held out plainly the answer to this mystery of balance: the ability to make one wing or the tail lift a little more or less strongly to maintain a steady course.

The Wright brothers spent long days watching birds flying over the Miami River near Dayton, Ohio, but later Orville Wright wrote: "We got plenty of flying fever from watching the birds, but we got nothing about their secret of balance."

Then, in June 1899, Wilbur Wright hit on the idea of twisting the wings of a glider to control their lifting power and balance. This was the first step toward the aileron that controls the balance of a plane or glider. It was the key that unlocked the door to flight. Later the Wright brothers recognized the use of the same principle in a photograph of a gliding gull.

Since that time the development of the slow-motion camera has made it possible to see and understand bird flight in a new way.

The plane is modeled after the bird, not only in its fundamental principles and construction, but even with its special devices, its slots and flaps, its reversible and variable pitch propellers. These devices have been worked out through countless experiments, and many fatal accidents might have been avoided if their use by the birds had been recognized and understood earlier.

The flight of a bird may appear to

The modern camera can catch the stroke of a flying bird's wings at any angle

be a series of confused, rather meaningless motions. But with the help of some hints from the slow-motion camera, these motions can be followed even with the naked eye, in birds from the size of pigeons and larger. One can see flight as a harmony of beautifully coordinated motions, each performing a definite function, each preparing the way for the next.

Each part of the wing, each separate feather is especially built and shaped to play its own particular part in this teamwork. The shape of the wing and the shapes of the feathers during flight are different from their shapes when the wing is outstretched but at rest.

When one understands something about the flow of the air over the wing and the energy released by this flow, one can begin to see how the rapidly changing curves of the feathers during

BIRD   221

a wingbeat are designed to capture this energy and make use of it. One then also understands how the structure and shape of the feather at rest enable it to take the proper, very different shape to function against the pressure of the air.

If one looks at the primary feathers of a bird's wing tip—that is, the propeller feathers—he sees that they have a wide vane behind the quill or shaft, but a narrow one in front. The quill acts as a pivot for the feather. When the wing beats the feather downward, the pressure against the air twists this wide rear vane upward, and the feather takes on the very subtly designed shape and function of a propeller blade, driving the wing forward and pulling the bird after it.

Even these quills are all different. Some are straight, while some are bent at right angles and stand up vertically

Ibises and herons soar in the air after being flushed from a saltwater marsh

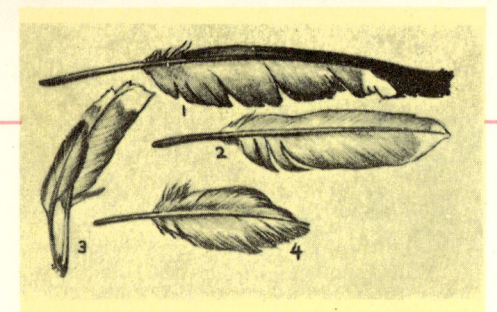

Each feather in each group is shaped somewhat differently. Even the quills have their special shapes, strengths and elasticities to make each feather play its proper part in flight.

These main feather groups are overlaid by covert feathers with many different shapes, sizes and positions, some standing nearly perpendicular to the wing surface—each one contributing its special share to give the wing its most efficient shape for lifting.

These feathers from a herring gull wing show (1) an outer primary with curved quill; (2) an inner primary with straight quill; (3) a secondary with its covert curved to give wing proper thickness for streamlining, and (4) a scapular feather which fills in the gap between the wing and the body

The secret of the feather's efficiency lies in the design of its quills and vanes. The vane of a feather is made up of rows of parallel fibres called barbs. They are long and narrow and stand out from the quill like the teeth of a comb, pointing slightly toward the tip and spaced well apart to allow plenty of room for play when the feather bends. This magnified section of feather shows the barbs (black lines) sloping out from the central quill.

from the wing's surface. Between the two there are all degrees of curves. Some of these quills are round in one part, flattened in another, hollow in one part, solid in another and with grooves and ridges at strategic places—all designed to control and shape the twists and curves.

Each small covert feather on the wing plays its own special part in building the most efficient wing shape for lifting. The shoulder joint is designed to hold the wing without effort at the proper angle, which can be varied at will to add to either the lift of the main wing or the forward drive of the propeller. And the whole feathered structure is bound together by a beautiful design of membranes, muscles, and sinews that swings each feather through its proper positions to function throughout the thousand split-second changes of a wingbeat.

One of the most ingenious features of a feather is the design of the vanes. If the vane's surface were all one membrane it might wrinkle when twisted, or stretch out of shape, or become torn. Not so the feather. Its surface is made up of hundreds of fibers called barbs. They are flattened, with their sides facing each other, and they stand out from the quill very much like the teeth on a comb, but at a sharper angle, slanting more toward the feather tip. The shape of the barbs varies at different parts of the same feather to give the right amount of strength or twist or streamlining.

Like the teeth of a comb these barbs are spaced apart from each other so there is plenty of room for movement as the feather bends. But they are held together by rows of tiny hooked fibers, with their barbules and barbicels that interlock to give a very elastic and almost indestructible surface. If two barbs are separated, a good shake or a stroke of the bird's bill will bring the hooked edges together again and the vane is as good as new.

When one looks at a feather, one sees, not the shape that will be used in flight, but the design that will produce any one of a great many different shapes as they are needed to meet the fast-changing conditions during flight. Each change of air pressure will bring an automatic response from the feather.

Some feathers are not used at all in normal flight but come into play only for special occasions — maneuvering, soaring, or the difficult feats of taking off or landing. Then their value is out of all proportion to their size. For instance, the alula, a little tuft of feathers growing on the rudimentary thumb at the bird's wrist, tucks smoothly out of the way in ordinary flight but swings out into position for very low speeds. Remove this feather tuft from one wrist and many birds can neither take off from the ground, nor land without a bad fall. The alula is not valuable for its own lifting ability. It acts to direct and activate the air flow at a critical point on the wing, so that other feathers may double their lifting power under some conditions.

In the same way there are times when the slots between the feathers at the wing tip, by their control of the air flow at this strategic point, control the lifting ability of the entire wing. To a lesser degree, as each important feather deflects the passing air stream, its neighboring feathers are affected by it. Each feather, through the thousand split-second changes of a wingbeat, must always keep the right relationship to its neighbors.

These propeller feathers have the same type of subtly designed twist as the propeller blade of an airplane. They meet the air at different angles from hub to tip, and for the same reason: They are moving faster at the tip than at the base.

Each wing is designed to suit the living habits of its owner. The long, narrow, feather-light wing of the albatross is a splendid wing for gliding, a very

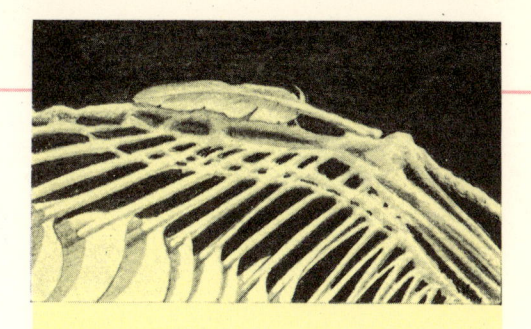

The underside of a herring gull's forearm showing finger, hand and wrist.

Above the wrist is the alula or rudimentary thumb, with one of its feathers controlled by three muscles. The hand and finger are controlled by sinews running out like tiller ropes over the wrist.

Below the hand, the membrane controlling the feathers, runs from finger tip to elbow. In the sketch it has been removed except for its lower edge, the white lines running below the hand bone.

The feathers of the hand are the primaries. The secondaries rest on the forearm. They show at the lower right each with its covert sloping above it, which adds to the curvature, determining its effectiveness as a lifting plane.

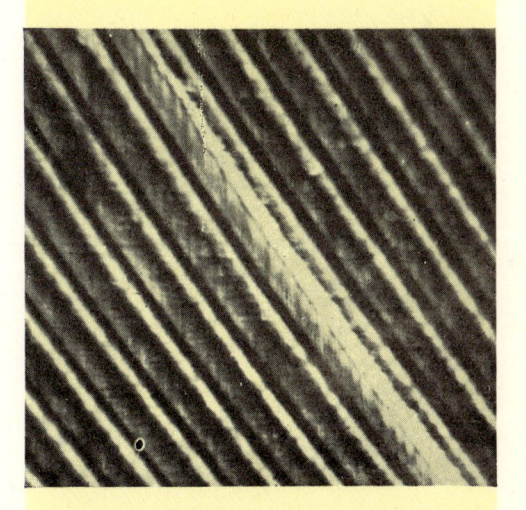

Section of feather vane with barbs separated. Solid black lines are the barbs. The shaded spaces between are filled by tiny interlocking hooked fibres (barbules and barbicels) holding the feather together yet allowing enough play so that it can twist without wrinkling. If two barbs are separated, a stroke of the bird's bill will bring the hooks together again. The diagonal white line in the picture is the opening between the separated barbs.

224 BIRD

poor one for flying. The short, heavily muscled wing of the pigeon produces a powerful flier but a poor glider. The broad stubby wing of the ruffed grouse is a rather inefficient flying wing, but can carry its owner through heavy underbrush where a better flying wing would soon be ruined.

Straightaway flight on a still day is an almost automatic action, guided by the design of the wing. The much more interesting features of flight, the tricky arts of taking off and landing, maneuvering and soaring, call for great skill and the use of special equipment.

An understanding of the principles of flight opens up a fascinating new realm of interest to the bird lover and field student. It offers one of the most spectacular and easily understood examples of the beautiful orderliness and design through all of nature.

Aerobatics

The ability of birds to maneuver to perform actions outside the ordinary routine of flying is one of the most interesting subjects in a study of flight. Yet it is one of the most difficult for photography or accurate description. The actions are apt to take place in a matter of split seconds, and the photographer who can catch and focus on the action within the range of his camera may count himself fortunate.

Among the various types of maneuver, some are merely playful, evidently just done for the fun of it. Others are skillful and thrilling shortcuts, as in the dive of a soaring wood stork or the meeting of a sudden emergency—an "air pocket" or a collision with another bird. Most exciting of all is the deadly serious business of attack and escape.

Watchers have thrilled at the sight of an osprey doing loops or backward somersaults in the air. On a bright afternoon, perhaps after a good catch has met the family's requirements for the day, one may sometimes hear the osprey's shrill call overhead. The bird

These sketches show the action of the propellers and the supporting wing:

1. The pressure against the air twists the primary feathers of this roseate spoonbill till they are nearly at right angles with the rest of the wing. They become propeller blades, driving the bird forward.

2. On the downstroke the feathers of the inner and outer halves of the wing slope in different directions. The inner half always slopes upward toward the front, downward to the rear, like the wing of a plane, supporting the bird as it glides forward through the air.

The outer half does just the opposite. It is pivoted on the wrist at its forward edge. The

seems to be hovering, but looking upward, not down toward the water as it would when hunting. It flies forward with rather labored flight, evidently trying to gain altitude as well as momentum. Then, with a sudden burst of speed it zooms upward with wings still flapping, until it is headed straight up and starts to fall over backward. It evidently does not enjoy testing its strength too far. The embryo loop will turn into a sideslip that will level off into straight flight again.

The bald eagle may carry this loop a little farther. At a nest near Jacksonville, Florida, the old birds seemed eager to impress all intruders with their prowess. When approached, they flew up, not very far, and started doing somersaults in the air. These birds would actually turn over on their backs and make a couple of wingbeats in that position. The motion pictures, too small to show much detail, give the impression that the birds lost little altitude in the pro-

pressure against the air twists the rear edge upward. The bird can control the angle of this slope to produce lift or forward drive as needed.

From the rear we see the light upper surface of the inner wing, and the shaded underside of the outer wing, showing this feature.

3-4. Here we have the beginning and end of the same stroke. On the down stroke the propellers drive the wing forward faster than the bird.

Starting from a position above the body the tips move forward by a full body length faster than the bird to a position below the neck. The air drives them forward, pulling the body after them.

On the upstroke the tips sweep back to their original position above the body, still driving the bird forward as they press back against the air, or they may just drift back with the air when a bird is in leisurely flight.

Throughout the stroke the inner half of the wing gives the bird a fairly uniform amount of support, keeping it at about the same level.

There is about one-ninth second interval between these two pictures.

Flight technique varies greatly with different birds built for different methods of living, but the principles remain the same.

cess and made little forward headway. The propellers seemed to be held nearly horizontal on the back stroke, which in this case would be the downward stroke, as though the lift were being gained from a downward push.

One of the most beautiful bird exhibits in Florida is a flock of several hundred white ibises stretched out in a long undulating line against a vivid blue sky. Sometimes one, two, or three birds together may drop from this line and fall head over heels, giving the impression of falling leaves as they whirl over and over, only to regain their balance after a considerable fall and fly back into line. This seems to be nothing but play, although they look completely out of control as they fall.

At other times these ibises may be returning to their rookery high overhead. Perhaps to make use of some favoring air current, they maintain their altitude until directly over the rookery. Then they dive downward and, at the right time, check their speed with their wings. As they descend, the head and legs are dropped straight downward, as though to help keep balance. A little above the treetops the wings rotate to an angle to give forward motion and lift, and the birds sail in, making a perfect landing.

The wood stork is apt to spend an hour or two at noontime soaring at a great height above the rookery. The birds bank steeply as they describe their great circles, the sun glinting off their white backs so that they stand out as dots of sparkling white against the deep blue sky. When their glowing backs are turned away from the observer, the shaded underside, reflecting less light, disappears completely and the birds become invisible until they reach the reflection point again.

It is hard to realize then, as one watches them, at what a sharp angle they must be banking to reflect the sun's rays from their backs into the onlooker's eyes. Suddenly a dark pinpoint overhead grows into a black spot. A wood stork is diving head first, with wings trailing out behind, close together, looking almost like a huge closed umbrella, whirling slowly as it falls.

Slowly the wing tips spread apart and, roaring through the air like a falling plane, the bird slowly levels off and coasts in to the rookery. It is hard to see how any feathers can stand the strain of such a performance.

The swallow-tailed kite, a much lighter bird, may make a different kind of dive and sudden stop. Even when a group of kites are high as to be almost out of sight, apparently the glint of a dragonfly's wing attracts the attention of one of the birds. Suddenly the kite will dive head first, with wings nearly closed but with wrists slightly forward and tips slightly away from the body. There seems to be no forward drive by the wings and no checking—a gravity dive but no doubt with guidance by wings and tail. Just above the treetops, so close that a smash-up seems inevitable, the kite spreads its wings, checking with a suddenness that wrenches them upward in a whirl of ruffled feathers. Its bill closes with a loud snap on the dragonfly and a couple of quick flaps restores equilibrium. It is a breathtaking and effective, though not very graceful, ending—the only hurried or ungraceful act a swallow-tailed kite indulges in.

At other times, if the dragonfly shifts its position, the kite will change direction during the dive. Then instead of ending in a perpendicular drop, the kite will swoop down at an angle and zoom up in a graceful curve, picking up the insect as it passes. If an insect is on the ground, the kite will often use a foot, instead of its bill, reaching down as it skims the surface and picking up a grasshopper without pausing in its course.

Diving into the water for a fish is more ticklish work and takes considerable skill. When an osprey sees a fish below, it drops one wing and turns sidewise, just as a plane does before going into a vertical dive. The wings are kept partly open to control speed and direction with the help of the tail until, at the last instant, the feet are pushed forward past the bird's head to strike the fish, claws first, in a smother of spray.

In an example of the osprey's perfect take-off, as the wings come to the surface they sweep backward on the first stroke, the outer halves turning over so that their upper sides face downward. A couple of horizontal strokes forward and back lift the bird straight up like a rising helicopter. A few feet above the surface, the angle of the wingbeat shifts and goes quickly into the regular flying stroke, and the bird hurries off with its fish.

In this take-off, after the wing tips leave the water, they do not touch it again but sweep parallel to its surface. Such a take-off, with soaking wet feathers, would probably be impossible for most landbirds. The osprey's first few primary feathers are deeply notched so that the propeller feathers can separate and open up the needed slots whether wet or dry.

The brown pelican uses a different technique for its dive. Depending on its bill instead of on its claws, it strikes the water head first. With its armored and streamlined nose it can make deeper dives and control the speed and depth of the dive with its wings. For a deep, fast dive the wings are not closed against the body but trail out straight behind the tail, giving the effect of a closed umbrella. As the bird strikes the fish it always turns, apparently catching the fish crosswise in the bill and breaking its back.

Movies of diving pelicans show most of the birds turning to the left, counterclockwise as they strike. The impulse for a left turn would naturally come from the right wing. Are most pelicans right-handed?

With its light body and webbed feet the pelican has no such problem as the osprey in leaving the water, but can take off in the conventional way by flying and hopping along the surface to get up speed.

One of the most skillful displays of maneuvering was put on by a turkey vulture when attacked by a pair of bald eagles. As the vulture flew past the eagles' nest, perhaps a hundred yards away, one of the eagles flew toward it, not very rapidly at first as though not wanting to arouse suspicion. The vulture kept on its course but, as it approached, the eagle suddenly put on speed. The vulture swerved sharply to avoid it and increased its own speed at the same time.

The eagle, much faster than the vulture, rose above it by perhaps 30 feet and slightly to one side, then dove with a powerful sweep of its wings. The vulture kept straight ahead until the eagle seemed just ready to strike. Then it dropped away from the eagle with a lightning flip of its wings and body. It seemed for an instant to swing under the eagle, and be suspended from the tip of the wing nearest the eagle. The eagle shot down harmlessly through the space just vacated by the vulture's body.

The second eagle of the pair had now joined the pursuit and by this time was overhead and diving before the vulture had regained its balance. The vulture righted itself, however, in time to repeat a side slip successfully. The eagles now took turns making short vicious dives at the vulture. Would it be possible for the vulture to recover from one dodge in time for the next?

Evidently the eagles did not anticipate the possibility of deflection. Their aim was to be in position to strike the vulture in its side slip, although they must always have aimed ahead of it to compensate for its forward flight. The vulture, meanwhile, put on speed between dodges. It stretched its neck in a most unusual fashion and flew with

This sequence of photographs shows the maneuvers of great horned owl as it approaches a landing spot in an oak tree

fast wingbeats toward a palm hammock. The eagles, after a few rapid sweeps through the hammock, gave up the chase.

Another feat of dodging, where the small wingspread made the vulture's method impracticable, was put on by a barn swallow. It was flying off the cliffs of Bonaventure Island when a pair of peregrine falcons, or duck hawks, attacked it. The hawks attacked in nearly vertical power dives; the swallow continued on its course until the last possible split second. Then it turned sideways with wildly fluttering wings. The hawk shot past it, and zoomed up to be in an overhead position almost before the swallow had regained its level flight. The hawks took turns diving, with one always in position to head the swallow away from the shelter of the cliffs. After some narrow escapes, the swallow got away and the hawks gave up the chase.

On one occasion a peregrine falcon flew up to look over a trio of young ospreys in the nest. The parent osprey flew at it and the peregrine turned away. Whether the falcon was using its top speed may be questioned, but the osprey kept pace with fast wingbeats, both elbows and wrists appearing considerably more bent than in normal flight, perhaps to cut down the leverage and drag of the full wingspread at such high speed.

The peregrine kept within a few hundred feet of the ocean surface. The osprey would get slightly above it, then lunge forward and downward while the peregrine shot sidewise and upward, apparently with plenty of power in reserve for a wide sweep. The osprey kept on, and in straightaway flight was able to follow and make several such attacks before both birds were out of sight.

Flying backward might seem to be in a class with stunt flying, an ability seldom needed or used by a bird, except perhaps in a fight. A slow-motion picture made of a pair of snowy egrets shows them fighting in the air. During this flight one of them flew backward for several strokes without losing its altitude. The wing motion was nearly horizontal, forward and back, much the same as the helicopter motion used by the osprey in its rising take-off from the water. The chief difference was that, on the forward stroke, the wing's lower surface struck the air a little more directly and at a steeper angle, thus giving more backward pressure than lift. The fighting egret kept its body in an almost vertical position, ready to shelter its head behind its forward snapping wings, or to kick its opponent in the face if it came too near.

The hummingbird uses backward flight when it wants to withdraw its long bill from a flower. Using the same principle as the egret, but able to rotate its wing more freely, it easily becomes a bird helicopter.

Most birds smaller than a pigeon have such rapid wingstrokes that it is impossible to study their flight without the aid of a camera. But the aerobatics and flight processes of larger birds offer a fascinating new field of bird observation. With some knowledge of how birds fly and of the air itself, one can interpret the wonderful art of flight that is so much a part of the general interest in birds.

Wings and the Air

Like water, the air has weight. Fourteen cubic feet of air weigh over a pound (.0765 lb. per cu. ft.). There is so much air above us that at sea level it presses against every surface that it touches—from all sides—with 14.7 lb. to each square inch.

Out of this weight and pressure of the air a bird develops the power to lift and carry itself forward. To do this successfully it must move through the air with the least possible disturbance. Every eddy of air that it leaves behind absorbs energy and cuts down its ef-

Gulls are experts in flight, twisting and turning in search of seafood

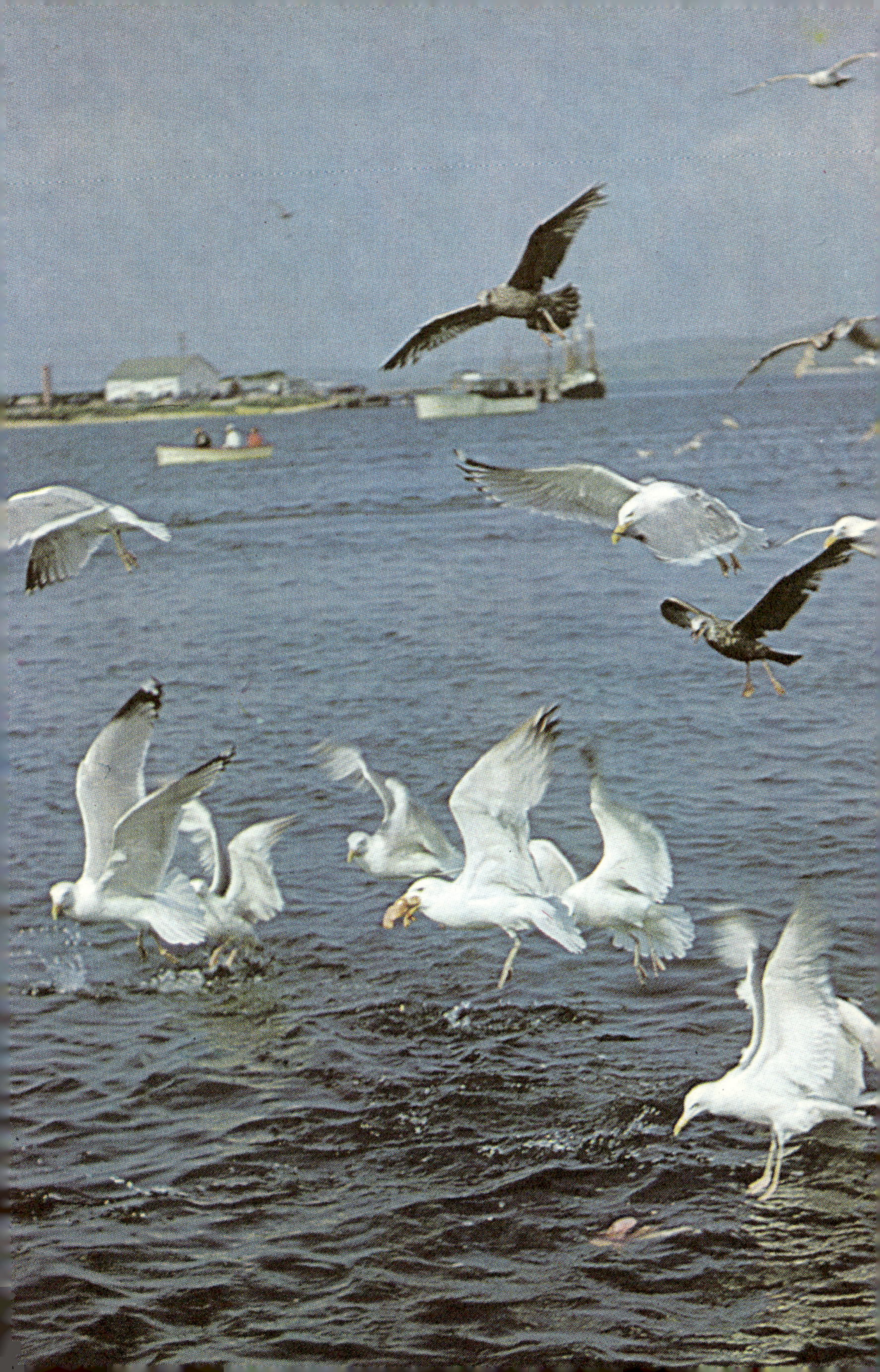

230 BIRD

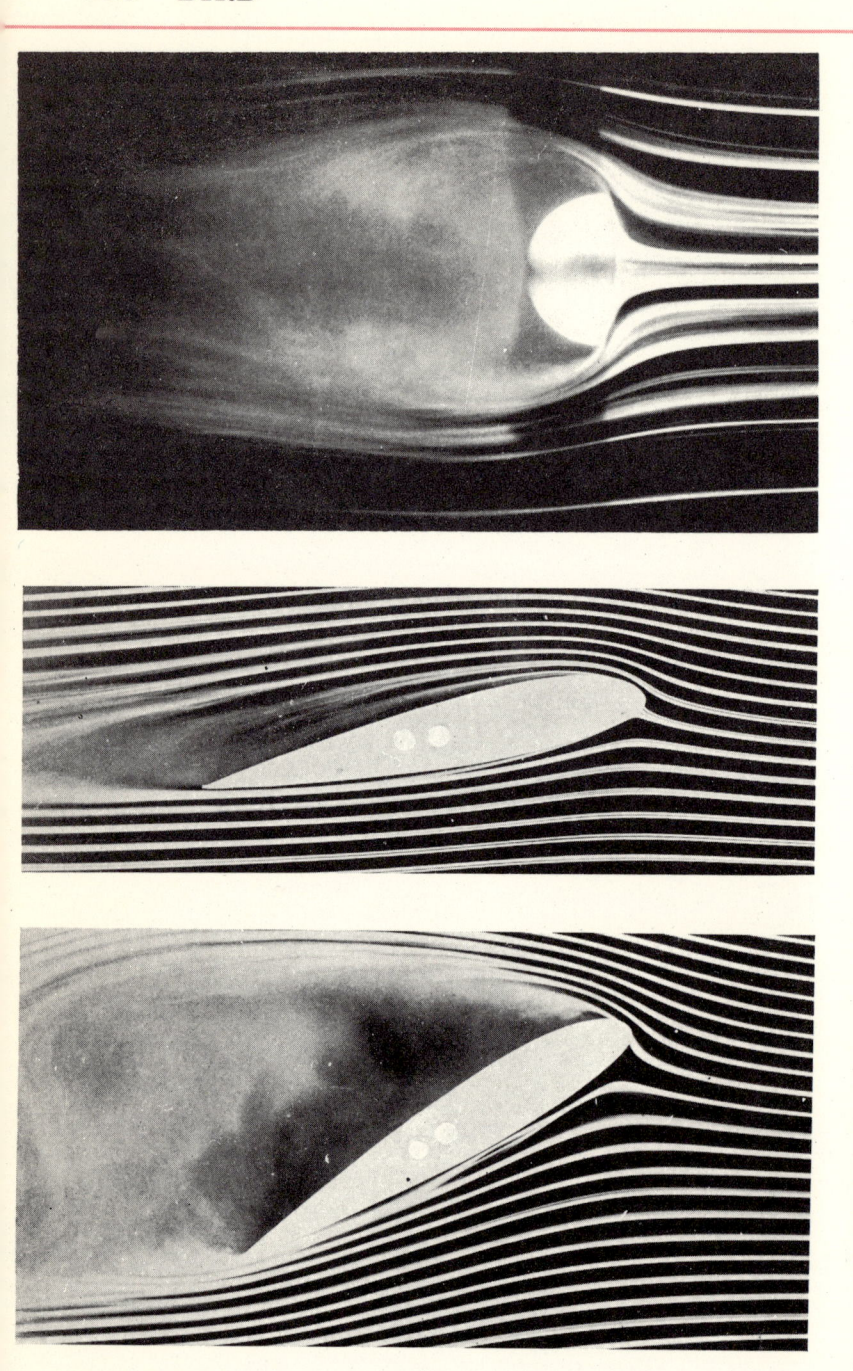

In the top picture the white lines are jets of smoke following the moving air stream as it strikes a half sphere (the white object) in a wind tunnel.

The white lines thicken against its face showing how the air is slowed down, increasing the pressure against the face of the obstruction.

As the air flows around the object, it leaves an empty space behind it. This is an area of very much reduced pressure. The fine curling lines show where little wisps of smoke are eddying into the partial vacuum. The main lines of the smoke stream gradually draw together again far to the rear. There is high pressure against its front, low pressure against the back surface. It would take a great deal of power to drive this shape through the air.

In pictures 2 and 3, the white lines of the smoke streams show what happens to the air when the wing stalls. In picture 2, the air stream has already begun to break away from the upper surface of the wing near its back. The stall has started. Notice that the smoke striking the lower front edge of the wing rises and divides, part of it going up over the top, forced up there into the area of low pressure by the high pressure below. At a lower speed this wing could be tilted more without stalling.

Notice that the wing's top surface accounts for most of the change in pressure —the lifting power—and that the lift moves toward the front edge of the wing as the angle of its tilt increases, tending to throw it off balance. The shape of the wing controls this movement of lifting power. If the wing is tilted too much the air can't follow down the slope of the upper surface. The lifting power disappears and the wing is said to be stalled.

In picture 3, the wing has passed the stalling point. The air has broken away from its upper surface. The smooth smoke streams have broken up into eddies. The lifting power has turned into backward pressure or "drag."

BIRD 231

The feathers of a bird's wing are shaped to give it the proper streamlining and curves to develop lifting power. Near the front edge the small covert feathers stand up vertically from the skin, then bend backward at right angles to build the right thickness. Behind the forearm the secondary and covert feathers grow in pairs, each secondary with a curved covert arching over it. The curves are arranged so as to give the cross section of the wing the curved taper of a plane's wing, the chief difference being that the under side of the bird's wing is concave, a more efficient lifting shape at low speeds. The plane wing's underside is slightly convex (see opposite models), a better shape for high speeds.

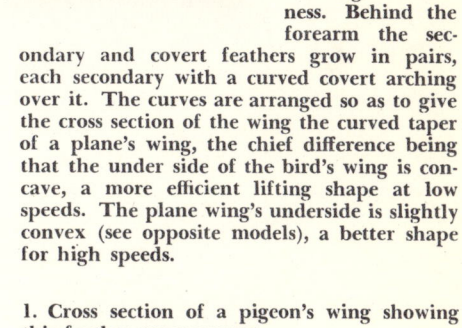

1. Cross section of a pigeon's wing showing this feather arrangement.

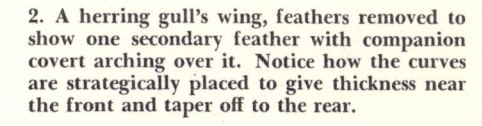

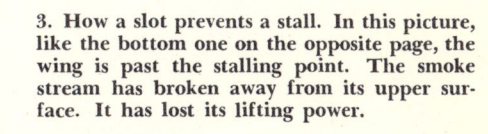

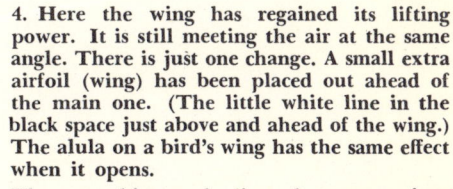

2. A herring gull's wing, feathers removed to show one secondary feather with companion covert arching over it. Notice how the curves are strategically placed to give thickness near the front and taper off to the rear.

3. How a slot prevents a stall. In this picture, like the bottom one on the opposite page, the wing is past the stalling point. The smoke stream has broken away from its upper surface. It has lost its lifting power.

4. Here the wing has regained its lifting power. It is still meeting the air at the same angle. There is just one change. A small extra airfoil (wing) has been placed out ahead of the main one. (The little white line in the black space just above and ahead of the wing.) The alula on a bird's wing has the same effect when it opens.

The two white smoke lines that squeeze into one as they go through the slot between the two wings must flow faster in going through this small space. This added speed reduces the pressure over the wing. The picture shows the result.

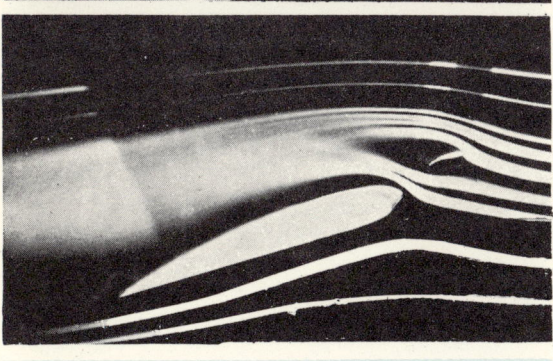

5. A landing brown pelican shows the alulas (airfoils) and slotted wing tips in use as the wings of a living bird duplicate the wind tunnel diagram.

ficiency. Air that eddies is air out of control and thus of little use as a source of power.

So the first essential to flight is a streamlined shape, one that fits itself into the natural lines that the air follows in flowing around it. This streamlined shape can be seen and photographed by putting some object in a wind tunnel and letting jets of smoke blow past it. The smoke follows and marks out the streamlines, the path of the moving air stream.

In the following pictures it can be seen how the air reacts to a wing moving through it; the airflow pictures were taken by the National Committee for Aeronautics.

Soaring and Gliding

Of all the bird's powers in the air none has aroused more interest and wonder than its ability to soar. To see a bird rise into the air on absolutely motionless wings and disappear from sight seems almost a magical illusion.

It is now known how a bird accomplishes the feat of soaring, but it is sometimes hard to remember while watching a bird soar that actually it is coasting downhill on a current of rising air. The speed of its rise is the difference between the rate at which the air is rising and the rate at which the bird is sinking or gliding downward. The only known exception to this is dynamic soaring, whereby a bird is able to use its momentum for a short distance to carry it upward.

Something is known about the air currents in which a bird can soar. The wind striking a sail, the shoreline, or a mountainside, will rise to get over it. A bird can soar on this rising "obstruction" current. Some types of land will heat the air over them faster than others. A bare field or patch of sand will be warmed by the sun and heat the air above it more quickly than a forest or water. The heated air will rise and a bird can soar on it. This rising, heated air, or *thermal*, may be in the form of a huge bubble or it may be a solid column. An eagle or vulture soaring upward in great circles is spiraling within the area of a rising current.

Time spent near a wood stork rookery when the young birds are learning to soar reveals some of their beautiful tracery of the air currents. Throughout the day there may usually be a few birds flying over the nearby everglades. Apparently these birds are closely watched by their mates at home. As soon as one of these fliers finds a rising air current and starts to soar, there is a general flight from the rookery to join it. A hundred or more birds hurry over, just above the tops of the mangroves, and start flying in circles, evidently feeling for the rising air. As they rise higher where the lift becomes stronger, their flapping slows, becomes intermittent, then stops entirely, and the birds spiral upwards with motionless wings.

Sometimes, apparently in a bubble of rising air, they lift in a closely packed bunch, swirling and swinging across each other's paths like a swarm of bees. Again there seems to be a vertical pillar of air current, traceable by a towering column of soaring birds. Usually, if there is a strong wind blowing, the column of birds tilts downwind, the entire column moving along with the wind. As the birds reach the top of the air column they usually become tiny specks against the clouds, if not going out of sight entirely. They coast back in groups of twos and threes and dozens, wings motionless, holding their formation perfectly like a group of planes. Over the rookery they drop their legs, half close their wings, and raise their alulas high, evidently braking their speed to cut lifting power in order to drop to the rookery. Occasionally one, more venturesome than the others, may try a headfirst dive, making rapid half spins as it shoots earthward, always leveling off 200 yards or more above the surface.

Comparing the wood stork wingspread

(about five and a half feet) with the size of the air columns usually suggests an air column diameter of 40 to 100 yards, the height varying with the height of the clouds. Occasionally in a strong wind a few birds will sail horizontally dead against the wind. Gulls have been seen sailing in this same way, dead against a strong wind yet making fast progress and holding their altitude with motionless wings.

A very interesting study of air currents has been made by Alfred Woodcock at the Woods Hole Oceanographic Institution. It seems to bear out some experiments that were made in England by Chandra, Graham, and Mal. In their experiments smoke was used to show the outlines of different kinds of convection currents over a surface with a steady and uniform source of heat, which would correspond to the ocean surface.

The studies show that the size and shape of the air currents change a great deal with changes in temperature and wind speed, but the general pattern looks a lot like a great honeycomb made up of closely packed hexagonal cells or columns of rising air marked out by the smoke. Each column is a separate circuit of air motion, sometimes with the air rising in the center and moving down around the edges, at other times just the reverse—down in the center, up around the edges.

As the rate of airflow over the heated surface was increased, corresponding to an increase in the wind over the ocean, these cells began to tilt in the direction of the wind. Finally they lay flat and rotated about their axes. Each cell rotates in the direction opposite to its neighbor, one clockwise, the next counter clockwise, so that their sides where they adjoin move in the same direction—down on one side, up on the other.

Woodcock's studies of the use of air currents by soaring herring gulls—and including gulls many miles offshore—seemed to indicate patterns of air currents very much like the experimental ones of Chandra, Graham, and Mal in England. Through the summer, when the air over the ocean is warmer than the water, no gulls were seen soaring off the New England coast except in the obstruction currents over a ship.

In the fall, when the air became colder than the water, soaring began when the air became 2° C. (3.6° F.) colder than the water and attained a wind velocity of at least one-half meter per second (or a little over one mile per hour). Until the wind reached a velocity of seven meters per second, or about 15½ miles per hour, some of the gulls would begin to soar in straight lines while others still circled. As the wind increased to about 19½ miles per hour, the circle soaring decreased markedly. It stopped altogether when the wind was blowing at about 24 miles per hour. From then on the soaring was only in straight lines, suggesting that the air pattern had changed from the columnar cells to the horizontal rotating cells, with the birds soaring along lines of rising air between two rolling cells. With the wind blowing at 28 miles per hour the soaring stopped entirely, showing that the air patterns broke up at this speed. This accounts for the straight line soaring of the wood stork and gulls mentioned earlier.

By comparing the positions of gulls soaring in the same air cells at different heights, it was possible to estimate the air column's size, shape, and direction. At low wind speeds the rising air columns were nearly vertical and continuous, not just rising bubbles. As the wind increased, the columns would tilt in a downwind direction until finally they apparently changed into the horizontal rolling cells. The soaring gulls showed that both types of cells started within 100 to 300 feet of the ocean and extended upward to considerable heights.

Gulls' altitudes were measured (with a rangefinder) up to 2,000 feet but they were seen much higher. With wind velocities as high as 28 miles per hour gulls would soar past the ship to windward on motionless wings, gain altitude, and disappear in a few minutes.

In *The Auk*, official journal of the American Ornithologists' Union (April 1940 issue), Woodcock mentions two especially interesting observations. During a cruise to Bermuda in January 1939, the boat went through an area of cold air, 7° C. colder than the water. Gulls were soaring in the air during the whole day. Then followed a day with warm air, warmer than the water, and there was no soaring. The gulls either sat on the water or rode the up-currents off the ship's sails. There followed two cold days and again the air was filled with soaring gulls, even though the wind was at 28 miles per hour. Then two warm days again grounded the gulls, and there was no soaring.

Again, Woodcock speaks of watching gulls rising on the up-currents off the boat's sails. Then the gulls left these currents, and flew with active flapping, apparently in a search for air currents rising from the water. When an upcurrent was found, they would fly upward with it until they reached a point where it was rising fast enough to lift them without active flight, and they would start to soar. They could detect the start of these currents just a few feet above the water, but would have to fly upward from 50 to 200 feet before the current was strong enough to soar upon.

There is an interesting difference between the gliding birds of the ocean and of the land. Most of the sea gliders — the albatrosses, frigate birds, and gulls — have long, narrow, pointed wings, the most efficient wing for gliding. Birds having this type of wing seem to be associated with low-level gliding. The seabirds can soar to great heights when conditions are right but they seldom need to. When gliding is possible at all they can glide for long distances and do all their traveling near the ocean surface.

Landbirds that travel by gliding must depend on localized air currents, so they must climb to get the last possible foot of elevation for the long coast to their destination or to the next rising air current that will give them another lift. These birds, almost without exception, have broad wings with deeply slotted tips, just the opposite of the seabirds. This type of wing is generally considered by aerodynamic engineers to be less efficient both for gliding and for high soaring, and yet the best soaring birds — the condors, eagles, and vultures — all have them. The condor, soaring master of them all, has the deepest slots; about one-third of the entire wingspread is slotted. Upon the air currents sweeping up the slopes of its mountain home it can sail for hours, spiraling upward or gliding on a level course without ever moving a wing. It can vary the width of its slots but, except in a fast downward glide, it seldom closes them.

The tips of a soaring bird's wings are as deceptive to watch as a sleight-of-hand artist. The feathers are slightly banked, one above the other, highest in front, lowest behind. Therefore, at the proper angle from below and behind they mask each other and appear to be closed, only to open out again as the bird swings through its circle to show them from another angle. One should always remember this in watching a soaring bird.

The wood stork in its flight is a sort of link between the landbirds and seabirds. It usually flies with a series of flaps and then a glide on its momentum, with pointed wing tips and slots closed until its speed drops and it must flap again. But when the wood stork starts to soar, it opens its wing-tip slots like any other land-soaring bird. When a bird can use either type of wing at will and deliberately chooses the slotted type for soaring, there must be a good reason for its choice.

A number of reasons have been advanced other than the fact that provides

In flight, the condor varies the width of its wing slots to utilize air currents

a bird with straight gliding efficiency. The slotted tip probably gives a bird better control of balance among the treacherous mountain currents. A condor can pirouette and turn on a pinpoint when it slips out of its rising current, but so can an albatross. The slots help a bird to bank at low speed when it spirals within a narrow air column, but the bird uses them for straightaway soaring also. The bird may use them to "spill" lifting power when its air column is rising too fast, but it uses them too when it has just barely enough lifting current to keep itself going. The slots may be a compromise with the need to fly, allowing the landbird a somewhat shorter and more manageable wing. Yet the condor is probably as poor a flier as the albatross; each depends almost entirely on gliding for its travels. One may wonder if it is possible that the soaring bird still has something to teach the human flier.

One of the most spectacular kinds of soaring, seldom seen, is dynamic soaring, in which a bird uses its momentum to lift it. There is a place in the California mountains where several families of red-tailed hawks nest in the face of a long cliff at about 5,000 feet elevation. Not far away a mountain valley lies open to the prevailing west wind. A strong current of air rises from the hot floor of this valley, helped by the drive of the wind. The red-tails hunt over the valley floors far from their home cliffs, but seldom make the effort to fly up the long climb back to their nests. They sail downwind toward the rising air current while working up a terrific speed. Then they swing sharply around into the rising air column and face upwind with motionless wings set at a very high angle of attack, apparently near the stalling point with slots wide open, to build up a tremendous lifting power. With this they shoot upward almost as if they were riding a giant elevator. Two circles within the air column will boost them 2,000 feet or more and they can easily coast across the valley to their nests.

Here, from a seemingly calm atmosphere, the hawk has found the power to build up a terrific forward speed and then to burst out into a skyward ride, all with hardly the motion of a feather. If one begins to look into the air currents that supply such power, and the forces that cause them, he will find himself embarked on another of the fascinating side-interests in store for those who would understand bird flight.

—J.H.S.

Recommended Reading
Bird Flight—Gordon C. Aymar. Dodd Mead Company, New York.
The Flight of Birds—C. Horton-Smith, H. F. & G. Witherby, London.

Identification Methods

The difference between the appearance of a bird when seen in the field and when seen close at hand has often been noticed. Certainly birds do not change their colors as do chameleons, yet observers are not "seeing things" when they note that the same bird, in the same plumage, does not look the same. These variations can be attributed to the conditions under which the birds are seen and to the physiological makeup of the observer.

The first factors to consider are the observing conditions and the most important of these is the presence of light without which things cannot be seen at all. In insufficient light, birds appear dark and vague — so much so that what was thought to be a blackbird, as seen in the shade, may suddenly fly out into the sunlight and reveal itself as a cardinal. On the other hand, too much light makes it difficult, if not impossible, to see birds sometimes.

When a bird is illuminated from above, the darker upper parts appear light, and the lighter underparts appear darker. The result of this countershading is the illusion of flatness making the animal more difficult to see. This pattern of coloration was used during World War II to camouflage airplanes. Watching a hawk with this pattern of coloration circling high overhead, it seems to appear and disappear, depending upon the angle at which its wings catch the light. The most desirable position for accurate perception is with the sun behind the observer, since the side of the bird facing the observer is well illuminated and the observer s eyes are not dazzled by too much light.

The condition of the atmosphere may alter the appearance of birds by influencing the color of the light. On a bright sunny day the light is yellowish, making the illuminated parts of the bird seem lighter and warmer in color. The markings, too, become lighter and sometimes indistinct. The rest of the bird, which is in shade, appears darker and cooler in color, since it usually reflects the bluish light from the sky; however, this is not always true, as the reflected light may come from the warmly colored ground or leaves. The part of the bird that receives a glancing light will show the color closest to that described as correct for the bird. These colors and their names have been standardized and may be found in the book, *A Nomenclature of Colors for Naturalists and Compendium of Useful Knowledge for Ornithologists*, by Robert Ridgway. In this book colors for birds have been rated scientifically, which eliminates the confusion caused by vague descriptions such as "chartreuse" warblers.

At sunrise or sunset, when the color of the light sometimes becomes almost orange, it is not unusual to see a "pink" swan or an "olive" blackbird. Also, the amount of dust and water vapor suspended in the air affects the clarity of the atmosphere. The visual result for an

Black-poll warbler

Common tern

Lark bunting (left)
Snow bunting (right)

Indigo bunting

Dowitcher

observer is that the farther away a bird is in dusty or damp weather, the less distinct is its form, and the lighter and less intense are its colors. Fog, mist, or rain filters the light so that light-colored birds appear darker and dark-colored ones seem lighter, and they all tend to fuse into gray silhouettes. In a fog or a mist terns and shorebirds appear to be larger than they really are because the silhouette effect produced by the diffused light obliterates their color pattern. It also obliterates the light and shade patterns that ordinarily break the appearance of the overall shape into smaller shapes, some of which blend into the background and make the entire bird appear smaller. Under these conditions what appears to be a hawk silhouetted against the sky can actually be a butterfly.

In a field the spots on a bird may seem to be stripes if they are close enough together. They may appear as an even tone, or the stripes may disappear entirely if they are small and seen from some distance. This visual phenomenon can also be seen in printed halftone pictures in which the image is composed of very small dots of different sizes. Almost everyone has seen a male yellow warbler but unless one is very close to the bird it is difficult to see its fine reddish-brown streaks. On the other hand, from a distance the elongated spots on the breast of a brown thrasher may appear as stripes.

Color contrast has an important effect on our visual perception. A light-colored bird seen against a dark background appears larger than it actually is, and a dark-colored bird against a light background appears smaller.

The reason for this optical illusion is that light-colored objects reflect more light than dark objects, and they also tend to radiate the reflected light so that it seems to impinge on the edges of the dark background. Another illusion resulting from the color contrast between a bird and its background is that a bird may appear lighter or darker, without the light changing, if it is seen against a background which is lighter or darker than itself. For example, an indigo bunting may seem to be light blue-black in color when seen against dark foliage but blue-black in color when silhouetted against a light sky.

Every color affects, and is affected by, the color adjacent to it. If the color of a blackbird contrasts sharply with its background it will appear more intense in color or tend to reflect the opposite, or complementary, color. A scarlet tanager never looks so brilliant as when seen against a background of green leaves. And a white tern seen against a blue sky may appear to have the pinkish bloom of a roseate tern because the complementary color of blue is orange (which looks pinkish when very light). When the color of the light is very strong (i.e., at sunset), or the bird is close to a highly reflective surface such as sand or water, the color of the illuminating or reflected light will obliterate this effect.

The second basic factor that determines the visual appearance of birds is one's own psychological interpretation of what is seen. When the American knot turns sideways and appears to change into a dowitcher, it is not a case of one bird changing to another species, but an observed foreshortening of the bill that is misinterpreted.

As one's knowledge of the mechanics of variation in the appearance of birds increases, one's perception becomes more accurate and one becomes a more reliable observer. This applies not only to birdwatching. The witnesses to a hit-and-run automobile accident generally disagree upon the color of the car that got away, and victims of a holdup are not always sure of the height of the gunman. All in all, part of the sport of birdwatching is the challenge to one's power of observation. —W.W.F.

Audubon Bird Guides — Richard H. Pough.

BIRD 239

Doubleday & Company, New York.
A Field Guide to the Birds—Roger Tory Peterson. Houghton-Mifflin, Boston.
How to Know the Birds—Roger Tory Peterson.

Signet Pocketbook, New American Library, New York.
A Pocket Guide to Birds—Allan D. Cruickshank. Washington Square Press, New York.

Filtered light affects the apparent color and size of birds. Terns sometimes appear larger in a fog because the diffused light obliterates their color pattern. (Common tern, from Audubon's Elephant Folio*)*

House wrens using an old hat for a nest, from Audubon's Elephant Folio

Nests and Nesting

Winter is an excellent time to begin a study of birds' nests. When the trees are bare of leaves, one realizes, by the old birds' nests in the forks of limbs, that many different birds have been living in the neighborhood. Many of these same birds will be back the following spring. Since it is a habit among them to return year after year to the same nesting areas, a sketch that indicates the location of the old nests will suggest where to look, in spring, to observe the actual process of nest building as it takes place.

All songbirds, and their eggs and nests, are protected by federal law. The United States Fish and Wildlife Service interprets this to mean that during the nesting season nests and eggs are protected and cannot be collected without a federal and state permit under any circumstances. The service has ruled, however, that nests collected well after the nesting season are not taken unlawfully. Therefore there is no harm in collecting old nests from trees and shrubs in winter. With the exception of a few of the larger birds of prey most birds build a new nest each year.

Examining an old nest closely is interesting and fun to do. The number of pieces of grass or twigs found in some nests is truly amazing. The materials used in the construction of a nest made by one species of bird, and the proportion of sticks, grass, and plant down, is typical of all nests made by that species. However, there are often unexpected things incorporated, such as man-made items, that were included because they happened to be handy to the bird when the nest was being made.

A collection of birds' nests and nesting materials (mud, grass, sticks, plant down, reeds, bark, plant fibers, horsehair, straw, spiders' webs, feathers, rags, paper, string — to mention the more common items) will make an interesting exhibit. It is possible for a nest collector to try "growing" some nests. Use nests of ground-nesting birds, such as those of the meadowlark or song sparrow. These usually contain seeds and, if the nests are collected late in January after the seeds have had a chance to mature, the seeds will sprout from the nests. A shallow depression is made in the soil of a flowerpot of suitable size. The nest is set on top of the pot, watered, and placed in the light.

The Nesting Season

Horned owls are among the first to nest. They incubate their eggs in February while snow still covers the ground. Including those birds that raise second and third broods, the nesting season comes to a close about mid-August. During the nesting season three billion pairs of birds are estimated to be rearing their young in the deserts, mountains, valleys, prairies, forests, swamps, lakes and coastal shores of North America.

Yellow-breasted chats building a nest, from Audubon's Elephant Folio

242 BIRD

Birds Nest Where they Feed

Nesting sites and feeding places usually coincide. These vary according to the habits of the more than 600 species of birds native to North America. Some of the warblers, for example, feed among the leaves in the tops of trees and build their nests high up among the branches. Ground-feeding sparrows nest on the ground or within a few feet of it. Woodpeckers that chisel their grub dinners from decaying trees, hollow out nest cavities in convenient dead limbs. Kingfishers tunnel into soft banks along the streams or ponds where they fish.

Nests Vary with their Builders

Nesting materials are obtained from a relatively small area adjacent to or within the feeding grounds. These materials, as well as the construction of the nest, vary considerably among the different species. There is the loosely made nest of the cardinal that has scarcely enough twigs in it to form a platform for the eggs. Another insecure nest is the large untidy mound of grass and weeds carelessly piled up by the house sparrow. The depression at the top is often so slight that eggs and newly hatched young come tumbling down. In contrast to these is the sturdy well made nest made by the robin for its brood of four, and the neat, round grass nest of the song sparrow.

A very interesting nest is the cliff swallow's small "mud oven" that is stuccoed to the side of an overhanging cliff or under the eaves of a barn. A protruding opening in the side serves as both entrance and window. Another remarkable nest is the deep, purse-shaped nest of the Baltimore oriole. It begins as a grassy collar suspended from the tip of a swaying branch. This is gradually deepened to form a lacelike bag about eight inches long. Then the fine weaving by the female oriole begins. She tucks long fibers in from the outside, then pulls in and pushes out from the inside of the nest until a sturdy basket has been made.

Another distinctive nest is the pendant cup of the red-eyed vireo. This is made of shredded bark fastened together with spiders' webs, the whole nest being hung from a forked twig.

Some birds have a sort of trademark, a bit of nesting material used exclusively by themselves. For example, the great-crested flycatcher almost invariably manages to weave a bit of snakeskin into the sides of its nest, although a strip of cellophane is often used by it as an acceptable substitute.

The cowbird solves the nesting problem by not building any nest at all. The female cowbird waits her chance to lay an egg in a temporarily vacated nest of another bird, usually a smaller bird, and then abandons the egg, leaving the incubation and the rearing of the young to be taken over by foster parents (*See under Cowbird*).

Three Essentials in Identifying Nests

1 The type of habitat in which the nest is found, such as a wood, swamp, or open land.

2. The precise location of the nest, that is, whether it is found in a tree or shrub, and its height from the ground; and whether it is located in the crotch, in a forked twig, on a limb, or against the trunk.

3. The shape and size of the nest, and the kind of materials used in its construction.

Many nests of many different species are so similar to each other that without information on all three points it is impossible to name the bird that built the nest. For some nests, even with full information, the only sure way to determine the species is to see the bird build it.

Country Birds Move Out

One sometimes hears it said, "We no longer have many birds around us; the

A female hummingbird feeds her hungry young

house sparrows and starlings have driven them out." More often the truth of the matter is that conditions have changed and the neighborhood has become more urban. The country birds have had to move out. Perhaps the brook whose shallow shores provided them with drinking and bathing places is now a deep ditch with cement walls; the fields and woodlands have given way to new streets and homes; the natural park has become well groomed—it has lost its dead wood and, with it, all the woodpeckers and other cavity dwellers, and it has lost its undergrowth that formerly provided cover for much of its wildlife.

On the farm there may have been changes detrimental to birdlife. Perhaps the shrubby fence rows have been cut off so cleanly that the birds that feed in the fields on weed seeds and grubs no longer have a safe retreat in the hedgerows.

With the present increased interest in soil conservation and the consequent introduction of strip farming and reforestation of lands unsuited to agriculture, and the increased protection of woodlands from grazing with the consequent increase in the number of sapling trees, and the amount of undergrowth, more and more wildlife may return once again to cultivated regions.

Three Requirements

If the three requirements of nesting birds are kept in mind — food, water, and cover — one can help the bird population increase greatly in even a comparatively small area. Correctly built birdhouses can provide nesting sites for some of the cavity dwellers. Suitable planting will not only increase the supply of food and cover but add to the beauty of the landscape. Birdbaths and fountains can provide water. Building a songbird sanctuary in one's neighborhood can be made a fascinating project (*See details under Plants and Water for Birds*).

—D.A.T.

Recommended Reading

Birds and Their Nests—Olive L. Earle. William Morrow, New York.
Bird Houses and Feeders—National Audubon Society pamphlet.
Birds in Your Backyard—Ted Pettit. Harper Brothers, New York.
Birds' Nests Field Guide—Richard Headstrom. Ives Washburn, Inc. New York.
Birds' Nests of the West Field Guide—Richard Headstrom. Ives Washburn, Inc. New York.
Handbook of Attracting Birds—Thos. B. McElroy, Jr. Alfred A. Knopf, New York.
Look for a Bird's Nest—Robert Scharff. G. P. Putnam & Sons, New York.
Songbirds in your Garden—John K. Terres. Thomas Y. Crowell Publishing Company, New York.

244 BIRD

Least tern nest *A newly hatched roadrunner sprawls in a nest of sticks*

The ring-necked pheasant lays its many eggs in a nest of grasses

The snowy egret constructs a nest of coarse sticks in a clump of reeds

The nest of the robin is a beautifully woven cup of grasses and sticks

246 BIRD

NESTING HABITS OF COMMON SPECIES

ROBIN—Almost anywhere in forests, open land, farmland, villages, cities; usually in trees but also in and around buildings, usually 10 to 15 feet above ground but as high as 70 feet. Nest is a small bowl of twigs and grass with inside floor and walls of mud lined with grass. Eggs, usually four, greenish-blue. Incubation: 11 to 14 days, usually by female; two or three broods.

CHICKADEE—In forests, open woodlands, parks, or orchards; in tree cavities from 1 to 50 feet up; sometimes in bird boxes. Nest is 3 to 12 inches deep; sometimes an old woodpecker hole, or hollow excavated by chickadee in decaying stump, and lined with moss, plant down, or feathers. Eggs, usually six to eight, white speckled with brown. Incubation: 11 to 13 days by both sexes; one to two broods.

HOUSE WREN—Usually around human habitations, in tree hollow, nest box, or small cavity in building, 8 to 10 feet from ground. Nest is built of sticks and lined with grass, hair, or feathers. Eggs, 5 to 12, pinkish-white, spotted with reddish-brown. Incubation: 11 to 13 days, chiefly by female; one to three broods.

BALTIMORE ORIOLE—On farmlands or along highways in orchard or shade trees (often in American elms). Nest is a neatly woven bag suspended from the end of a limb 9 to 90 feet from ground; made of woven plant fibers and hair and lined with plant down or similar warm material. Eggs, four to six, grayish-white and variously marked with brown and black. Incubation period: 14 days, chiefly by female; one brood.

SPARROW HAWK — Along woodland border, in orchard, and in cavity of building, along village or city street; usually in hollow tree, sometimes in rock cavity or hole in bank, in a birdhouse (in the West it may use old grass nest or deserted crow nest); commonly no nesting material used save what may remain in cavity from former occupant. Eggs, usually five, white mottled with brown. Incubation: about 29 days by both sexes; one brood.

FLICKER — In orchards, forests, open woodlands, shade trees. Nest in hollow excavated by the flickers in tree or fence post, also nests in bird boxes, a bank, or cavities in buildings, height from 2 to 60 feet from ground. Eggs, usually five to nine, white and glossy. Incubation: 11 to 16 days by both sexes; usually one brood.

NUTHATCH — Usually in old woods, but also in orchards and along tree-lined streets, 2 to 60 feet up. Nest cavity (often old woodpecker hole, or in bird boxes) lined with shreds of bark, grasses, leaves, feathers. Eggs, five to eight, creamy-white, somewhat spotted with reddish-brown. Incubation: 13 days by female; one brood.

SCREECH OWL — In forest, orchard, or shade trees, in hollow tree, nest box, old woodpecker hole, or in building, country or urban. Nest lined with whatever material already present or nearby: straw, leaves, feathers, etc. Eggs, three to five, white and smooth. Incubation: 21 to 30 days, largely by female; one brood.

BARN SWALLOW — Around farm buildings or villages not far from water, or in crevice in cliff, stub of old tree, on ledges under bridges and wharves. Nest is made of mud and straw, lined with soft grasses and feathers, shaped like half a shallow cup and stuck to sheer wall or on some projection (beam in barn). Eggs, three to six, whitish and spotted with brown. Incubation: 11 days, largely by female; two to three broods.

CHIMNEY SWIFT — In hollow trees but commonly in chimneys. Nest, a half saucer of twigs stuck together and to the chimney wall with the dried gluelike saliva of the bird; placed near top of hollow or chimney or perhaps as much as 20 feet down. Eggs, four to five, white and glossy. Incubation: 18 to 22 days by both sexes; one brood.

GOLDFINCH — In scattered trees in open country, often in fork near end of branch or top of small tree, four to 20 feet from ground. Nest, a cup made of fine grass and usually lined with thistledown. Eggs, five, bluish-white. Incubation: 11 days by female, one brood. One of the last birds to nest, usually not nesting until July.

YELLOW WARBLER — In shrubs and low trees around farmlands, three to eight feet from ground, usually in fork or crotch. Neatly made nest of gray plant fibers and shreds of bark, lined with plant down. Eggs, three to five, grayish-white, spotted with brown or purplish. Incubation: about 10 days by female; one brood.

HUMMINGBIRD (ruby-throated) — In forests or in open, about cultivated lands, 3 to 30 feet up on trees or shrubs. Nest a tiny cup three-quarters of an inch in inside diameter made of plant down and trimmed on outside with bits of moss and lichen. (Anna's hummingbird of the West makes a similar structure, similarly located.) Eggs of both species, two, white. Incubation: about 16 days by female; one to two broods.

MEADOWLARK — On ground in open country, usually in slight depression. Nest is made of grasses and weeds; lined with finer grasses and often arched over so that eggs are concealed; sometimes a grass-covered tunnel leads to it. Eggs, usually five, white, spotted with brown. Incubation: 15 to 17 days chiefly by female; one brood (perhaps two broods in the south).

SONG SPARROW — On ground or low in bushes, usually near water. Nest is made of grasses, weeds, bark, and lined with finer grasses, sometimes fine roots and hair. Eggs, three to seven, variously light-colored and finely dotted with red-brown. Incubation: 10 to 14 days, chiefly by female; two to three broods.

GREEN-TAILED TOWHEE — Usually on ground in brushy land or open woodlands with undergrowth. Nest is made of leaves, strips of bark, weeds, twigs, and grass, lined with finer grasses, pine needles, and hair. Eggs, four to six, white, dotted with red-brown. Incubation: 12 to 13 days, chiefly by female; one to two broods. —D.A.T.

Leach's petrel lives far out at sea and visits land only to nest in a burrow

Birds of the Ocean

Seabirds have become the masters of the most fearful habitat of all, the most trackless wilderness in the world, the abode of terrible storms—the blue, limitless ocean.

V.C. Wynne-Edwards first suggested that the ocean was the safest habitat in the world for any animal that was able to solve the fundamental problems of living there. The simplest of these problems is that of turning the winds and waves to an advantage. Once a bird can make slaves of the sea winds, it has at its disposal a feeding ground stocked with all manner of edible life. Furthermore, the ocean is distinguished from almost all other of the birds' feeding grounds by the almost total absence of competitors, predators, and enemies.

Since seabirds cannot nest at sea, a substantial part of the yearly life of adults must take place away from certain oceanic breeding grounds—even though the pelagic, or oceanic, species may fly some hundreds of miles, and possibly even a thousand, from their nests when they are incubating eggs. Beyond this limit in the breeding season the ocean birds discovered will be all nonbreeders, which means that nearly all of them are young. The evidence is strong that adult seabirds of all kinds, except a few large albatrosses, attempt to breed every year. In May, June, and July in the North Atlantic, when the adult fulmars are incubating eggs or managing partly grown young, there are still great concentrations miles out of reach of any known breeding colony—for instance, on the Newfoundland Banks. Such evidence as there is of the nature of these birds is that they are young, and it now seems likely that the period of adolescence of a fulmar may be as much as seven or eight years. That of some albatrosses is eight or nine.

However, it is clear that many ocean species fly great distances even when incubating eggs. All seabird pairs share in incubating, and most take approximately equal turns. The periods of time spent on the eggs by most tube-noses (albatrosses, shearwaters, petrels, and fulmars) may be from four days to a week, or even longer. The incubating bird lives on its fat reserves and gets considerably lighter during its incubating periods. To fly its great distances it needs mobility and endurance, and it needs endurance also to starve during its days on the nest.

While at sea, the problems of mobility and endurance have been solved by the oceanic seabirds through becoming "sailplanes" rather than power craft. This fundamental fact, which must be obvious to aviators and was probably realized by many seamen in the days of sail, has been widely overlooked by ornithologists, and probably was not properly pointed out until Wynne-Edwards did so in 1935.

If the oceanic seabirds relied entirely on power flight, they would be able to operate to the feeding grounds only in calm weather, and through the accumulation of large amounts of energy by means of food consumption. In fact, seabirds in the breeding season tend to do the opposite. They remain at their land stations in calm weather, and it is quite probable that they would find it difficult and exhausting to get from land to the middle of the ocean in calm weather. Their motive power is provided by the natural winds of the great oceans deflected from their waves.

The evolution of the most important group of the oceanic seabirds—the tube-noses, including the petrels and albatrosses—has, judging from the present distribution of the members of the tube-nosed order, taken place in the South Pacific and in the neighborhood of the Antarctic continent. In those seas, nature's winds blow hardest and most continuously, and the great rollers, swells, and waves are almost permanent features of the surface of the waters.

It has been suggested that the absence of albatrosses in the northern Atlantic may be due to the fact that the equatorial waters of that ocean are rather permanently calm and not capable of providing the albatross with the lift necessary for them to glide their way through and establish themselves on the other side. Actually, about a dozen individual albatrosses belonging to five species have been recorded in the North Atlantic Seas (*See Albatross*).

In ordinary rough weather, apart from the exercise of the controlled surfaces of the seabird's wings and tail and small shifts of its center of gravity, no important work is done by the bird at all. It uses the components of the wind reflected from the banked sides of the waves and swells, and moves distances by alternating the use of this lift with excursions into the sheltered trough between the crests of the waves that is out of the main windstream. It contains various moving air systems, which are consequences of the impact of the windstream on the irregular surface of the sea. Sailplanes cannot sail directly against the wind, any more than a sailing yacht can, but they tack and zigzag to advance against the wind in much the same way.

Besides becoming sailplanes, the oceanic birds also become "camels," in the sense that they have become adapted to going for long periods without food. It seems quite clear that they all either drink saltwater or do not drink at all. It is known that they can live for several weeks without food, though most species seldom starve in normal life for more than a week.

With some tube-noses, the young can be neglected in the nesting burrow for about a week without anything worse than a certain delay in their fledgling period. Many species of gannets and tube-noses and a few other seabirds feed their young on fatty foods until they have a weight considerably greater than their own. The parents leave the young alone on the ledges, molt, and then disappear away to sea. The young wait on the cliffs to finish their growth, losing weight all the while. They find their own way to the sea, often in a glide, and only to teach themselves the final details of the art of flight afterward. They work their way out to sea as quickly as possible, though it would be crediting them with unbirdlike intelligence if one were to suggest that they knew that the sea was the safest place.

The only really important predators of seabirds are man and certain animals like rats that have been introduced by man at seabird breeding stations. The numbers and importance of other predators are not great, and their effect upon the population of their prey is small, and often negligible. The effect of the numbers of prey upon those of the predators is, on the other hand, well marked. However, at every important North Atlantic seabird station there is a small but often varied community of animals that are predators on the individual members of the main community or their eggs or young. Ravens snap up young that fall from the cliffs or dispatch adults that meet with accidents. Crows nest on the bird cliffs, poach eggs, and pick up what they can get. Peregrines sometimes become specialized in attacking some seabird prey at their breeding islands. On at least one Welsh island the little owl has been recorded as preying on storm petrels. But the chief parasites and predators of seabirds are also seabirds—skuas and gulls.

In the Antarctic, the local great skua takes a steady toll of other seabirds. In Britain the predatory role of gulls has been exaggerated, but in other parts of the North Atlantic—as the eastern seaboard of the United States, and Holland—they have made a serious difference to the numbers of other seabirds by usurping their breeding sites, as well as by direct predation. In Britain, gulls skim a crop of eggs and young that the community can usually spare, and some of which it might have lost from other causes (*See under Predation*).

Many of the true birds of prey, such as eagles, goshawks, sparrow hawks, have been recorded as taking seabirds. So, too, have snowy and eagle owls. As a whole, their predations are quite insignificant. Mammal predation is more serious. In some parts of the world, foxes definitely confine the members of the local bird colonies to the inaccessible parts of the cliffs. Occasionally, and not importantly, fishes have been

Gannets nest in large colonies

known to prey on seabirds. Angler fishes have taken cormorants, shearwaters, gulls, and auks; cod eat cormorants and auks.

Parasites appear to have very little effect upon the number of seabirds. There is no evidence that external parasites control the numbers of their hosts. Very little is known about the physiological effects of internal parasites, particularly of bacteriological and virus parasites. However, it appears that these last two are the most likely to affect wild populations. A virus disease of Manx shearwaters has been recently described in Britain, and it certainly kills a few in the crowded colonies every year. The most important seabird disease, so far identified, is psittacosis, which in the early 1930's spread through the vast population of fulmars nesting in the Faeroes and Iceland (*See Parasite*).

The important limiting factor in the lives of seabirds is food. Very little is known about this, although certain species, such as shags, cormorants, and terns, have been investigated to see if they were serious competitors of fishermen. It is not a question of the seabirds limiting the numbers of fish so much as the fish limiting the numbers of seabirds.

Once it is through the years of youth, the seabird is an experienced animal that presumably has an excellent knowledge of feeding grounds, geography, meteorology, and navigation. It can unquestionably look forward to a long life—perhaps in some birds a life as long as that of man. It can go about its business on the high seas with an ease and reliability that man has come to imitate only very recently, with equipment of the utmost complexity and at colossal expense. —J.F.

Do Birds have a Sense of Smell?

The question of whether birds have a sense of smell increases in interest yearly as more research is done on it. Early naturalists never doubted that birds could smell. Then came discoveries that disproved this statement beyond all doubt. More recently, investigations on various species have shown that some birds do indeed have this faculty in a limited degree, and others may have it as well.

It is now quite certain that a great majority of birds have little or no sense of smell, although some species have. It is too early to be dogmatic, for this is a field in which much more investigation is needed. Direct practical experiment rather than observation of wild birds seems likely to offer results, although many experiments have been inconclusive and disappointing.

It was thought that birds could smell easily quite early in their evolutionary history and indeed today reptiles have a well-developed sense of smell. Then, owing to birds' aerial existence, coupled with the extreme development of their sight and hearing, this faculty may have atrophied.

Through sheer lack of use or the need for use, the faculty disappeared from many species and only lingers on in some. Certainly birds in general do not need to smell in the way that most mammals need to. The power of flight of birds, together with their first-rate vision and hearing, may have done away with the need for odor detection.

Yet, all birds have olfactory nerves leading to the brain from the sensory surface of the nasal chambers. Whether these are vestigial remnants of the past when birds could smell is not clear. Further complicating the question is the fact that every bird has a preen gland. This gland varies in size and in the potency of its secretion, which—to human noses, at least—has a distinct odor. Of what value this odor is, no one yet knows.

Pycraft, a British ornithologist, suggested (but with no evidence) that it was by this smell that birds might recognize each other. It is well known that many birds distinguish their food by means other than sight or color, in this way avoiding poisonous berries, while eating harmless ones of the same appearance. It is known, too, that vultures appear to detect carrion from ranges beyond the power of vision.

The problem is intensified by the fact that human beings have a relatively poor sense of smell. Also, the science of scent, as it is known by man and as animals generally utilize it, has been insufficiently studied.

The approach to the problem of bird scent is derived from a number of serious but unspectacular experiments, a few sketchy but interesting observations, and a mass of surmise and conjecture based on opinion and visual tests. One of the most thorough studies is W. G. Walter's 1943 paper, "Some Experiments on the Sense of Smell in Birds. Studied by the Method of Conditioned Reflexes."

At Amsterdam University, Walter experimented with siskins, parakeets, and ducks by applying the methods made famous by the Russian physiologist, Ivan Pavlov, with dogs. Yet, in no instance could Walter obtain a conditioned reflex linked to smell as the necessary conditioning stimulus.

Walter rightly pointed out that even where satisfactory reactions are observed, these may not, in fact, be due to smell at all, and may be the result of sight, hearing, or even some little-understood sense. Unfortunately, his work did not cover flesh-feeders, where the sense of smell might conceivably be strongest.

At the Gloucestershire, England, headquarters of the Wildfowl Trust, Peter Scott has directed experiments on the relative sense of smell of ducks and geese. At one time wild geese were credited with a good sense of smell. Reliable observers, even though in a minority, still claim that the greylag goose

Experiments on geese have not settled the questions of their sense of smell

can pick up human scent, especially when the bird is wary on its nest.

The wildfowl sanctuary experimenters noticed that as two observers passed directly upwind of a small party of white-fronted geese feeding unconcernedly with some teal at 20 yards' range, the teal took flight instantly, whereas the geese seemed unaware of the proximity of human beings. Other experiments with geese all showed their extremely poor or nonexistent sense of smell.

Rooks and starlings seem unaware of the pungent odor of smoke when it surrounds them. Nesting rooks have perched blissfully amid clouds of aromatic tobacco smoke puffed at them from a foot or two away. Starlings show no annoyance when the smoke from chimney pots smothers them, although there is some evidence that they are aware of it and deliberately perch on chimneys to bathe in the acrid fumes.

Domestic poultry dislike garden bonfire smoke intensely and avoid it at once. At the Abbotsbury, Dorset, England swannery, one of the largest and oldest in Europe, the hundreds of swans never touch the poisonous great water dropwort plant that grows abundantly near their quarters. If given it when captive in a cage, they eat it and die.

Many English birds can detect the poisonous berries of cuckoo-pint and avoid them, although they eat other fruits that look almost identical. One aviculturist found that his finches and siskins deliberately chose certain seeds they like from among other seeds that they dislike, even though they look identical in every respect.

Dugald Macintyre, a Scottish gamekeeper naturalist whose opinions are highly respected, claims that ravens and peregrines both can smell well. From a lifetime of experience with these two species, he believes that they can detect human scent on traps and carrion where there is no possibility of sight or hearing coming into play.

Other birds that experimenters have shown may be able to smell to some degree include pigeons, magpies, some of the owls, and some crows. The question of vultures is still an open one but the evidence indicates that they hunt almost entirely by sight. It is difficult to imagine that scent can carry a mile or more, whereas the acuity of bird vision has been proved many times to extend even farther than that.

The answer to part of the problem lies in the close affinity between taste and smell. It seems possible that a number of birds have had the faculty of smell reduced and retain it only for tasting food. Except for this they cannot smell as mammals do, and a great many birds have not even this reduced sense.

The one marked exception seems to be the New Zealand kiwi, which has been fairly successful in hunting by scent. But the kiwi has the special provision of nostrils at the end of its downcurved bill. No other bird has nostrils thus situated, and the kiwi, therefore, appears to be a survivor of an earlier age when birds might have detected odors with ease. —Da. G.

Bird Songs
The Songs of Thrushes

In North America there are no bird songsters to compare with the woodland thrushes. The mockingbird, which shuns the woods, compares in technical brilliance but it does not have a song in the sense that the thrushes do. The mockingbird specializes in notes and variations, in the production of striking and beautiful single tones or phrases, but it lacks melody. It arouses delight and astonishment, but the singing of the wood thrush, the hermit thrush, and the veery evokes wonder.

When one listens to their songs with an attentive spirit, at twilight from the depths of the forest, it seems at times as if one hears something more than a singing bird. This is especially true of the veery, which is a less brilliant singer than either the wood or hermit thrushes, but more unearthly.

The hermit thrush is the only thrush that winters in the United States. The others winter in Central and South America. It is strange that birds of such sheltered habitat should launch themselves overseas twice a year—flying so close to the waves that from a ship at

The song of the wood thrush can be heard two weeks after its arrival in spring

sea the traveler may occasionally glimpse a brown speck fluttering in the trough—and yet survive.

In the New York City area one cannot generally expect to hear the first wood thrush before the first week in May, when the bare trees of winter are already assuming their summer foliage. The veeries arrive about the same time, but do not begin to sing until a week or two later. The Swainson's and gray-cheeked thrushes are present by the middle of the month but have gone northward again by early June.

The song of the hermit thrush has much the same quality as the song of the wood thrush, though the form and melody are quite different. The song is not so rich and leisurely, though perhaps more ethereal and inspired. Instead of a deliberate succession of full rounded notes, interspersed with minor phrases, these are showered on the evening air with a wonderful rush of energy, all in one sparkling cascade after another. The notes are thin and pure, a succession of falling phrases in different keys, dropping down and down, then beginning all over again from the summit of audible pitch.

Some feel that the song of the wood thrush is marred, or brought short of perfection, by the light and seemingly impromptu phrases interspersed between the flutelike passages. They feel that these touches are often unmusical and somewhat harsh, and so take away from the perfect music of the flute-tones. But there is extraordinary interest in these grace notes and trimmings and a sort of uncanny, unearthly beauty that is lacking from the purer tone of the main phrases to which they serve as foils.

The ease and leisure of the wood thrush's song is one of its characteristics. The bird is never shaken with the effort that a house wren is. Usually it sits motionless on a branch, at rest. Every few seconds (with the regularity of some marvelous mechanical toy) it

The hermit thrush, a beautiful songster, spends the winter in the United States

lifts its head, opens its bill, and delivers itself of a brief phrase, and then subsides until another phrase has formed and is ready to well up within it. The song is discontinuous and never finished. A little *hip-hip* usually introduces the principal phrases. These phrases generally consist of three or four flutelike notes bound together. They are followed immediately, as a rule, by a muted trill—then silence.

The wood thrush, in keeping with its boldness, has accommodated itself to cities. It is at home now, like the catbird, wherever there are shade trees and shrubbery. But it is the only one of the five North American species that has done so.

Veeries are often found in swampy woods that border large marshes, and in wooded ravines. In June one can hear them just at dusk in such places, calling softly to each other. They cannot be seen, ordinarily, unless one is looking for them, and they are apt to fall silent as one draws near. If they are alarmed by the presence of a human being, they utter a very softly whistled *whew,* that cannot be heard unless one is very near the bird. It is deceptive, and sometimes it is necessary to watch the movement of a bird's throat to be sure it is uttering the sound at all. When disturbed, a veery does not puff itself up and raise the feathers of its head like a wood thrush. It remains quiet and inconspicuous, no matter what might give it cause for alarm.

The song of the veery is a soft and continuous swirling sound that gives the impression of spiraling downward. American ornithologists differ on how it should be rated, and understandably so, for it is not comparable to the song of any other bird. It is not brilliant or spectacular, nor notable for range and variety—these being the qualities that are usually dwelt upon when one thinks of birds as rivaling each other in song. The veery's voice is merely uncanny and unearthly.

It has a soft, reedy double tone, such as might conceivably be produced by a violinist drawing his bow across two strings at once; but no mechanical instrument could produce such thin, resonant chords. It has also a windy quality, and perhaps one could give an idea of it by comparing it to the sound produced by blowing across the top of a bottle.

The overtone, the resonance, as if the bird carried its own echo within itself, might make one think that the song was actually issuing from inside a bottle. Heard in the gloom of twilight, back and forth across the marshes, it gives the impression that this is no bird at all but some unknown spirit.

The season during which the song of the veery may be heard lasts less than 1 month out of the 12. Like the wood thrushes, the veeries arrive in the New York City area about the first week in May. They may then be heard calling, but not singing, two syllables that blend into each other, a sort of *weheu*—like the word *veery,* hence the bird's name. Sometimes only the second syllable is heard very faintly.

It is near the middle of May when the veeries begin to sing. Evening after evening, for the next three weeks, they can be heard if one goes to the right places. Toward the end, however, the songs become intermittent; the singers no longer persist in them. By the middle of June there are young in the nests and the adults no longer have the leisure to sing, or even to call to each other. One will not hear them again in the North until another spring arrives. —L.J.H., Jr.

Song Patterns of Birds

Each species of bird sings a distinctive song, differing from songs of all other species in some of the elements of *pitch, range, length, rhythm,* or *quality.* The arrangement of these elements produces pattern; therefore, one can say that each species of bird has its own distinctive *pattern* of song. Some are simple and easy to learn; others are complex, challenging one's resourcefulness to know them.

Individuals may vary the "standard" pattern by some change in one or even all of the five elements. One bird may even vary his own patterns—a mockingbird does. A song sparrow may have 20 or more variations to its theme, and among all song sparrows there must be thousands of possible variations. And yet it isn't difficult to recognize mockingbirds or song sparrows by voice, even though the pattern of song is so much varied.

One can watch singing western mea-

A song sparrow, its breast feathers ruffled by the wind, sings out

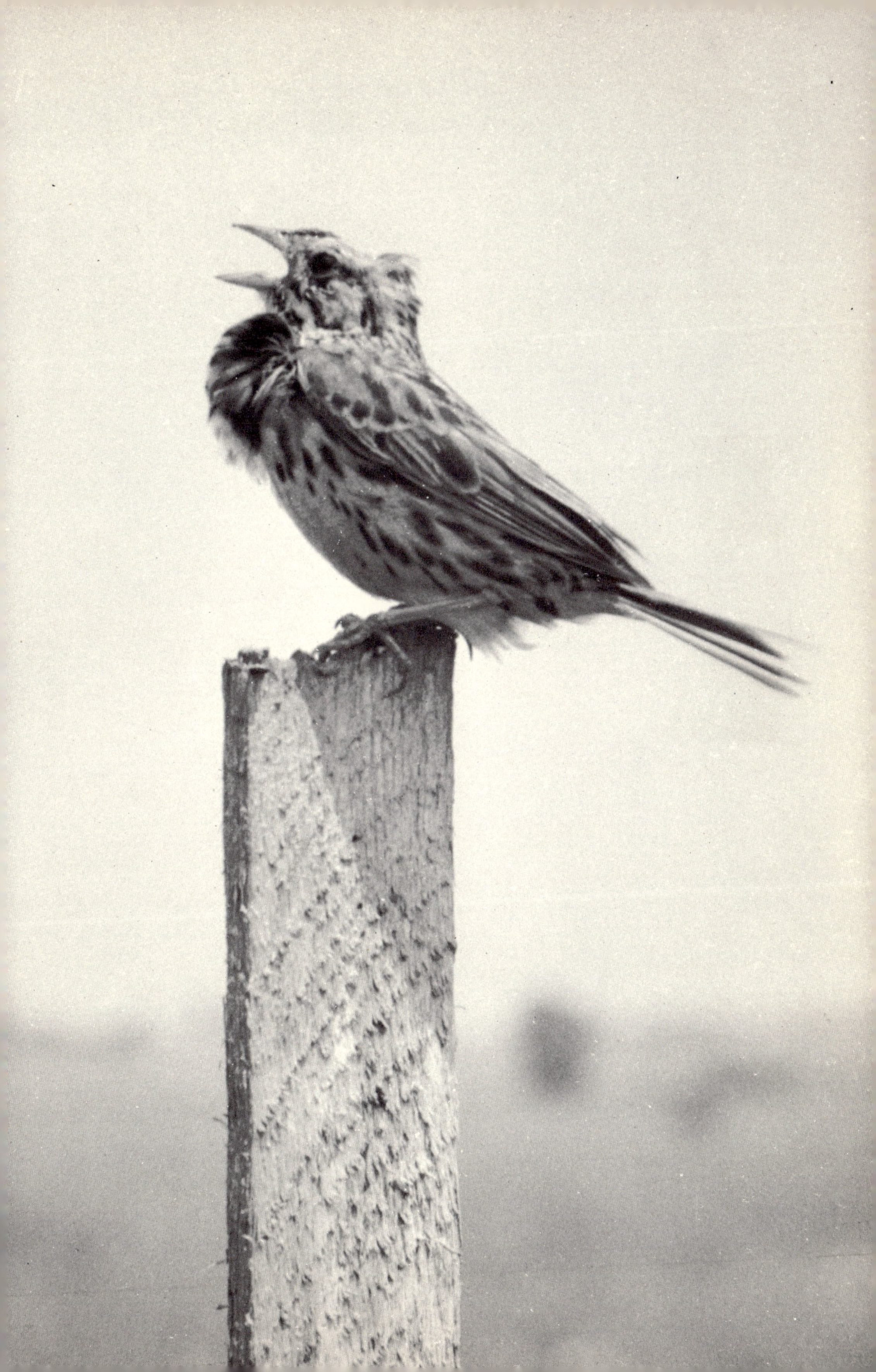

dowlarks and make a game of counting the number of times a bird sings one song before abruptly changing to another. At Fresno, California, a male sang six different songs in 40 minutes early one morning. The number of repetitions of each of his six songs was as follows: 15-13-29-13-5-20. Another meadowlark at the Salton Sea made quicker changes, doing five different patterns in 10 minutes, not one of which was repeated more than 12 times. Something inherently basic about each song made it easily recognizable as a meadowlark's.

One can think of these performances as the playing of phonograph records. One record is played a certain number of times and then is turned over. Certain favorite records are run more times than others and especially favorite records are called back from time to time. Once in a while a needle seems to scratch terribly.

Each species of bird has a distinctive annual singing pattern as well as a distinctive song pattern. *Time* and *place* are the key elements here. During the summer of 1939, when Arthur A. Allen of Cornell University, Ithaca, New York, was teaching at the University of California at Berkeley, he planned to bring the sound truck of the Albert R. Brand Bird Song Foundation to Yosemite Park for the Fourth of July weekend. He inquired whether he would get the songs of three birds—the Sierra grouse, the western tanager, and the Townsend's solitaire. He was told he could get the grouse and the tanager but he would *not* get the solitaire. When he asked why, the park naturalist declared that the solitaire never sings on the Fourth of July.

Allen arrived at night with his equipment and assistants and proceeded directly to the suggested location on the Glacier Point road. A day or two later he moved down to the floor of the valley and had an enjoyable campfire evening with the Yosemite School of Field Natural History. He had recorded the songs of the grouse and of the tanager but not the solitaire. He found a nest where parents were feeding young and set up the sound equipment but never a song was heard. The *place* was right, but the *time* was wrong. Allen was a week or more too late and at least two months too early for full songs. In September this thrush starts coming back into song, and in October juniper berries are ripe on sunny slopes of high mountains and solitaires sing out their beautiful songs.

A number of birds follow this same singing pattern: territory and mating songs on the nesting grounds in spring, then little singing when raising families in midsummer, but a resumption of song into winter. The brown towhee of the West demonstrates strange annual timing. It sings from early spring until mated, then stops.

Some birds sing during migration. A black-headed grosbeak has been heard singing in the Colorado desert on April 11. An advance company of eight males traveling north from Mexico, perhaps bound for Yosemite, stopped to refresh or orient themselves near the cool Andreas Canyon. The place and the time were right for just one of them to sing. Several days later a flock of 40 male Bullock's orioles paused in this same region but neither time nor place seemed right for song according to the established annual cycle of this species. Some migratory birds sing all season on the wintering grounds. Good examples in the American West are the golden-crowned sparrow and the Gambel's sparrow.

There are many other well-known examples of birds that remain in song practically the year round — mockingbirds, meadowlarks, quail, song sparrows, blackbirds, and most owls.

Still another type of bird *language* stems from physiological conditions. Baby birds in the nest chirp when hungry or impatient. Even these chirps follow a rather definite species pattern. When a few weeks old they come into better voice and food calls evolve, some

A female black-headed grosbeak and fledglings

of them quite musical. Here one thinks of black-headed grosbeaks and water ouzels.

At the age of three weeks, when they are as large as they will ever be, the baby-talk of black-headed grosbeaks grows into a sweet food call—a clear whistled *whee-you* of slurred pattern. In late July this is the only music of the family, for the adult male has given up singing. In August even this stops. Soon all go songless to Mexico and apparently do not sing throughout the winter. A caged black-headed grosbeak has been heard singing beautifully in September. By April the young male black-headed grosbeaks join other males for the journey back to the nesting grounds where they seem to arrive in full song. Each one seems to travel to its previous year's territory or, in the case of the young, to the birthplace. Principally by song, and at times by combat, they spar for a week or two until they are more or less equitably spread over their nesting territories.

Then it is time for the females to arrive. They are attracted by the songs of the males and, perhaps, by familiar surroundings. Songs of the males seem to increase in fullness and volume as nest-building begins. The male black-headed grosbeak is an industrious singer and worker. He helps gather and place the twigs and rootlets for the one loosely-built nest of the year. He also helps incubate the eggs and sings as he sits on the nest. (Only one other western bird is known to do this—the western warbling vireo.) Grosbeaks sing from high perches, low perches, or even on the wing, and for one-third the year—from mid-April until mid-July or from their arrival on the nesting grounds until the young of the year become self-sufficient.

Much more can be written on the subject of listening to birdsong, but learning from personal experience promises many hours of pleasure for anyone willing to try it. —C.A.H.

(*See also:* Bird Attracting under Plants and Water for Birds; Birds and Hedgerows under Hedgerow; Birds of Prey under Predator; Color Vision under Animal: Color Vision of Animals; Colors of Feathers under Feather; Disasters under Hurricane; Longspur; and Migration; Effects on Birds of Changes in Habitat under Animal: Animal Habitats of a Forest; Hibernation of Birds under Hibernation; Homing of Birds under Homing; also under Animal: Navigation of Animals; Migration under Migration: Secrets of Bird Migration; Parasites under Parasite: Some Insect Parasites of Birds; See also: Problem Birds; Protection of Birds; Roosting of Birds; Sizes of Birds under Facts About Birds)

BISON

Other Common Names — Buffalo
Scientific Name — *Bison bison*
Family — Bovidae (cattle, sheep, and goats)
Order — Artiodactyla
Size — Male: body length, 10 to 12 feet; height at shoulder, 5 to 6 feet; weight, 1,600 to 2,000 pounds. Female considerably smaller
Range — Originally lived from Pennsylvania west to Nevada and the Great Slave Lake south to New Mexico. Wild herds live today only near the Great Slave Lake and in Yellowstone National Park, Wyoming; many are kept on reservations and in parks elsewhere

Today the American bison, more often, but incorrectly, called buffalo, is known to most people only through the bars of a cage in a zoo, but this amazing animal was once lord of half the continent, ranging the West in millions, supplying the Indians with food and clothing, weapons, and fuel. When the white man reached the West he, too, lived off the buffalo and in return did his best to exterminate the creature, so nearly succeeding that it is a miracle it still survives.

Although the bison at one time roamed over most of North America, at least in the temperate regions, it was always most at home on the Great Plains of the West, and it was there that the white man first met the animal. So far as is known, the first civilized man to see the American bison on its native range was Cabeza de Vaca, a Spaniard who had been shipwrecked on the coast of Texas. About 1535, Cabeza, with three other hungry and forlorn men, made his way from some point on the Texas coast to the west coast of Mexico — the first transcontinental tourists. Somewhere on this incredible journey he met the "cows," as he called the buffalo, and wrote of them: "Their horns are small, like those of the Moorish cattle, the hair is very long and like fine wool and like a peajacket."

The American bison, a close relative of the European bison, is not a true buffalo, although it belongs to the same family, Bovidae. The family also includes cattle, sheep, and goats. True buffalo live in Africa and Asia, but the use of this name for the American bison is so firmly established and so much a part of the history of the West that the two names have become interchangeable through common usage. The American bison is one of the largest members of this family and is the most distinctive game animal in North America. A full-grown bull is a powerful animal measuring five to six feet at the shoulder, nine to nine and a half feet long, and weighing from 1,600 to 2,600 pounds. The cows are smaller, weighing from 700 to 900 pounds. The massive head, neck, and shoulders of the bison are covered with long, shaggy, black hair. The rest of the body is covered with a coat of shorter, dark brown wool mixed with hair. The distinctive hump is a bony structure, formed by the elongation of the dorsal vertebrae, and covered with layers of choice meat. The hump is very large. It extends over the shoulders just back of the neck, and tapers gradually back to the hips.

Bison are extremely hardy animals, able to survive winter blizzards and killing summer heat. Domestic cattle would have perished on ranges where the buffalo were able to live and thrive. Their eyesight is poor, but their hearing and sense of smell are keen. They will begin to move away from an enemy long before they can see it, warned of its presence by its scent. For some reason however, a buffalo is not frightened when another buffalo near it is killed; a fact of which both Indians and white men took advantage, by creeping up on the leeward side of a herd and killing until at last the animals grew alarmed and moved away.

In many ways American bison are

A few thousand bison still survive in western refuges

not unlike the domestic cattle of the United States but they are much hardier and live and breed for a longer time. The calves are born in the spring from April to June. The newborn buffalo calf resembles the domestic calf but is much more active and vigorous. It is able to follow its parents within a few hours after its birth. Even the very young calves have astonishing strength and endurance, and are playful and when very young are easily tamed. However, they soon develop the wild unmanageable traits of the adults.

The newborn calf has a yellowish-red coat but the color darkens quickly and in a few months it is almost as dark as that of its parents. The calf follows its mother for a year or more, until its place is taken by another. The maternal instinct is very strong in the buffalo cow and she protects her calf with fierce determination.

There are many reports of bison having been seen in the East during the early colonial period but by 1800 they had, for the most part, retreated beyond the Missouri River. There, on the Great Plains, they lived in millions, drifting in huge herds north and south in search of their favorite food, gramma grass and the short, sweet buffalo grass that grew "thick as hair on a dog's back." The buffalo is a thoroughly gregarious animal and the great herds were made up of many small herds, grazing in open formation. When alarmed, they closed ranks and stampeded in one compact mass. These herds moved in regular formation under the leadership of a tough old bull. The younger bulls ranged around the herd, giving the alarm if they scented Indians, and fighting off the wolves and coyotes that were always lurking to pick off a weakling or a stray calf. The cows and calves stayed in the center of the herd. When the calves were in danger, they were surrounded by a double ring, the cows forming the inner circle with the determined bulls on the outside. There are many written accounts of the great fights between young bulls, fights so bloody and so fierce that often both combatants died. The earth was said to shake from these battles.

However, contrary to these accounts, other observers state that there was very little fighting among the young bulls and the fights that did occur were not the earthshaking battles so dramatically described.

Normally, a buffalo herd moved slowly. Once in motion, however, nothing could stop it, although the herd could be turned aside. Men in wagon trains often stayed up all night shooting, shouting, beating on tin pans, to keep their wagons from being engulfed by a slow-moving herd. Railway trains sometimes had to stop for hours while a herd crossed the tracks. A stampeding herd was a terrible and a magnificent sight — deadly to any man or beast that might be caught before it.

White men usually ate only the tongue, hump, and hindquarters of the buffalo, but the Indians wasted no part of the creature's huge body. They ate everything eatable. They boiled the meat, baked it in a hole in the ground, made it into a sort of a sausage, or dried it to form buffalo *jerk*. This dried jerk was often pounded and mixed with buffalo tallow to make a pemmican that lasted for years and was highly nutritious.

The liver of the buffalo was usually eaten raw as soon as the animal was killed, and men eating it never suffered from scurvy, the most dreaded disease of the plains. The intestines were also eaten either raw or broiled over coals, and buffalo gall was sometimes added to water, forming a drink that some white trappers insisted was delicious. But the most prized part of the buffalo was the tongue. Thousands of these, dried and pickled, were shipped to eastern markets. In one year in the 1840's, 25,000 buffalo tongues came by steamboat down the Missouri.

Next to the flesh of the buffalo the hide was the most useful part, both to Indians and to white men. Indian women tanned them, a slow, messy process. They pegged the hide down on the ground, chipped off the fleshy part, scraped it, then rubbed it with buffalo brains. When the hide was soft and pliable they sometimes dyed it with colored clays and painted it with pictures. The hides were used for garments, blankets, tent coverings, saddles, battle shields, and even for small boats — the *bullboats* of the shallow western streams. Bullboats were made by stretching buffalo hides over a framework of willow poles.

The Indians made weapons of the larger buffalo bones, and needles and awls of the smaller bones. The women gathered buffalo hair, left on sagebrush when the animals were shedding, and wove it into halter ropes or made it into stockings. Buffalo horns were turned into handles for knives and into ornamental headdresses and powder horns; the hoof of the buffalo formed a mallet. And buffalo droppings, *buffalo chips*, were for years the primary fuel of the treeless plains, burned by Indians and white men alike.

Hunting for buffalo was the great sport of the West for both Plains Indians and white men, with this difference: the Indians usually killed only the animals they needed, the white men killed for the sport of it. This wanton killing of the buffalo by the white man was the greatest single cause of the dreadful Indian wars of the 1860's and the 1870's. The Indians, watching their food supply melt away under the bullets of white emigrants, grew hungry and then angry and at last went to war.

The Indians made a religious ritual of the buffalo hunt, with officers who managed the affair and fixed rules that the hunters must follow. A religious ceremony was always held before a large hunt. The Indians killed buffalo in various ways. Sometimes the animals would be driven into a great pen on the plains and there slaughtered; again, a young brave would disguise himself in a buffalo robe and lure a herd to the edge of a precipice, stepping aside just in time to keep from being pushed over the cliff by the crowding animals; often a lone Indian would creep up on a herd and kill until the animals grew alarmed and moved off. But the favorite Indian method of killing buffalo was the *surround*. Warriors on horseback, armed with the short bow (the best weapon, next to Colt's revolver, for killing buffalo), would ride around and around a herd, yelling and shooting; later they identified their own kill by their individual arrows.

White men used rifles and revolvers for killing buffalo and killed them so ruthlessly that long before the first railroad was built across the West in 1869 the herds had begun to vanish. The railroad finished the matter, for it provided cheap transportation of meat and hides to the East and it brought the professional hunter to the plains. Under the bullets of these hunters the buffalo herds disappeared like dust in a heavy rain.

These skilled marksmen never deigned to touch the animals they had killed, leaving the work of cutting up the carcass to *skinners* who took only the hide, tongue, and hindquarters, leaving the rest to rot. In those years a carrion reek hung over the whole West and the plains grew white with bleaching bones; it was said that a man might walk for a whole day over the bodies of dead buffalo and never step on the earth. Then, to harvest the bones came a strange, wild crew of men, the *bone pickers*.

Today, bison live in the wild only in northern Canada

Bison calves are born in spring while adults are still shedding their winter coats

Buffalo bones were worth from $6.00 to $10.00 a ton for fertilizer in eastern factories and the bone pickers fought violently among themselves for this harvest, staking out claims on bone piles as miners stake claims for gold, shooting to kill when another man jumped their claims. Then the bone pickers, too, went away, for the last of the buffalo had disappeared and even the buffalo grass began to vanish from the plains.

Of all the enormous herds that once roamed the West it has been estimated that in 1889 only 89 animals remained alive in the wild, only a few private herds in the United States and in Canada—and even these were melting away, preyed on by poachers. Barely in time the country realized what was happening. Game laws were tightened, poachers were punished and the buffalo were saved. The great herds have gone forever but the buffalo will survive—the most useful native animal this country has ever known. —D.G.

BITTERN
American Bittern
Other Common Names—Stake driver, pumperlunk
Scientific Name—*Botaurus lentiginosus*
Family—Ardeidae (herons and bitterns)
Order—Ciconiiformes
Size—Length, 23 to 34 inches
Range—Nests from central British Columbia, northern Manitoba, southern Ungava Peninsula, and Newfoundland south to southern California, central Arizona, Colorado, Kansas, the Ohio Valley, and southern New Jersey. A few breed in the southern United States. Winters chiefly in southern and Pacific states north to British Columbia

Perhaps the most peculiar of all marsh sounds is that made by the American bittern. Henry David Thoreau aptly dubbed the bittern "genius of the bog." It is a hermit, lurking in remote or inaccessible morasses, shunning contact with man or even with its own kind. Most herons associate in large groups, often numbering hundreds at nesting time, but one seldom finds more than two or three bitterns breeding in any square mile of wetland. In smaller patches of marsh a single pair is the rule.

The place to look for it is in the black water areas of marshes, amid cattails, pickerelweed, water lilies, arrowhead, and rushes.

Skulking in the morass it crouches as low as a muskrat and is equally inconspicuous. Sighting an intruder, the bird compresses its buffy plumage and apparently becomes a bit of weathered wood, its beak pointed skyward to match the tips of surrounding bulrushes. Dark stripes from throat to belly complete the camouflage. Standing thus, a bittern will watch a human for half an hour, motionless as its own background. Some scientists have even asserted that it will sway gently with the reeds whenever a breeze ripples through them. Whether or not this be true, the bittern, when disturbed, behaves in a

BITTERN 267

way to blend with the marsh. Its confidence in protective coloration and stance are such that one may approach it closely before it takes alarm and flutters away, with dangling legs and a squawk of expostulation.

The cry of the stake-driver is different from that of any other denizen of the marsh. Most audible during the breeding season, it may be heard in the morning, or more insistently in the twilight, but mostly in early spring. Sometimes, it calls throughout the summer and early autumn. *Chunk-a-lunk! Chunk-a-lunk!* is a tri-syllabic call readily heard a quarter of a mile away on still days. At farther distances the cry is cut to the last syllable, a sort of *Chunk* almost like the sound of an axe driving a stake in the mud, and giving significance to the familiar name of *stake-driver*. Often the notes remind one of an old wooden pump, obvious to any listener at short or middle distances, whereas the post

The American bittern is an inhabitant of freshwater marshes

driving is perhaps more convincing at long range.

The bittern subsists on snakes, tadpoles, newts, frogs, fishes, meadow mice, shrews, and crayfishes; also, insects, such as water boatmen, dragonflies, back-swimmers, grasshoppers, and various insect nymphs. On the lookout for such boggy provender the bird will sometimes stand without moving for 15 minutes or so. Then it will take a quick step forward and impale its unwary victim on its sharply pointed bill. At other times it stalks slowly about, stooping low and ever ready to spear its prey.

The bittern builds a platform of dead rushes about a foot in diameter on the floor of a cattail swamp, sometimes in a dry oasis but more frequently over shallow water. Deep, impassable morasses are favorite nesting areas, but one may find nests also around small but secluded ponds.

Here the female lays from three to seven eggs, but four or five is the usual number. They are somewhat glossy, vary from buffy-brown to olive, are elliptical ovate, and hatch in about 28 days.

The buffy young lack the darker markings of mature birds but look equally snakelike, hissing like adders and striking viciously at one's fingers. The female feeds them by regurgitation, each youngster in turn seizing the beak of the mother and holding fast until it has gulped down a salamander, slug, or perhaps a small horned pout. After feeding they flop on their sides as if exhausted and lie still for a quarter of an hour or longer. Then hunger stirs them again and they crowd along the side of the nest waiting impatiently for their mother's return with more food.

The brown of the male bittern's upper plumage is subject to one remarkable variation in the nesting season. On the back and shoulders a pair of ruffs, nearly white and shaped like wings, may appear. Ordinarily invisible beneath the wing coverts, these light plumes are

The female bittern lays from three to seven eggs in a clutch, but four or five is the usual number

obtruded for display, either during courtship or when the bittern tilts with a rival male. In combat, the spearlike beak is a formidable weapon which the Narragansett Indians used for arrowheads.

The American bittern is a primitive bird, perfectly fitted for life in the green world where it desires nothing but to be left alone, and where it will probably survive until the last bog is drained (*See Bog*). —H.M.H.

BIVALVE
Two-shelled Animals—The Bivalves

Whether it is clams, oysters, mussels, scallops—stewed, steamed, fried, or on the half shell, it is a two-shelled animal (a pelecypod, or bivalve) that provides the feast. Because of their popularity at the dining table, bivalves are one of the most familiar groups of marine animals. Bivalves are also well known because of their wide distribution. Freshwater forms occur in all great river systems, lakes, ponds, and even in ditches, streams, and marshes. Marine pelecypods live in all seas where animal life is known. The tidal flats of seacoasts are a favorite habitat. Visitors to seashores almost anywhere in the world can, by a bit of beachcombing over the sand and mud flats exposed at low tide, easily discover and observe an interesting variety of these animals (*See also under Seashore*).

As the name bivalve implies, the animals all have two shells, or valves. These are generally flattened and hinged on one side so that the shell can be opened or closed. The shells often have strange forms. There are the long, knifelike razor clams, the fluted scallops and cockles, and the spreading, fanlike *Pinna* and *Solemya*, with their long, impressed, radiating lines. Many are colorful and have beautiful patterns. They vary in size from tiny clams less than half an inch long (seen in sandy, freshwater ponds, and streams) to the giant *Tridacna* of the Indian and Pacific oceans which have shells over five feet long and weigh more than 500 pounds. The bivalves form an interesting and important part of most shell collections.

All bivalves have an enveloping cape, or mantle. This comes in two parts, as does the shell, and forms the shell lining. It is this mantle that builds the shell as the animal grows. The shells themselves have three layers: a thin, horny, skinlike outer layer, often brownish in color; a thicker prismatic layer made of calcium carbonate, which gives strength; and an inner, smooth, lustrous layer of pearl. Any irritating foreign substance—a grain of sand, a bit of broken shell, or perhaps even a small fish—that becomes lodged inside the shell, likewise gets a coating of pearl. In a few years, after a series of these coatings, a grain of sand may become a true pearl.

Most pearls of commercial value come from marine clams and oysters, although some beautiful pink pearls are obtained from freshwater clams of the Mississippi Valley. The value of pearls is determined by their size, color, and luster, and many hundreds of shells may be opened in order to find a single pearl. A process of commercial pearl farming has been developed whereby an irritating substance is inserted within the bodies of oysters which are then left in the water for two or three years until they have had time to form pearls. The oysters are then harvested and the cultured pearls of commerce extracted.

The name *pelecypod* means hatchet foot and refers to the shape of the foot of some of these animals. The foot is a muscular organ that can be extended out of the shell; it is used to propel the animal through the sand or mud in which it lives. It moves slowly along by extending the foot into the sand; the tip swells to serve as an anchor. Then the animal draws itself forward and repeats the process. Some clams, such as the surf and razor clams, have a more highly developed foot which they use for leaping forward through the water. These clams make particularly interesting subjects for observation in an aquarium. Mussels have a special gland in the foot that secrets tough threads or fibers by which the animal

The mussel is a common bivalve

can attach itself to rocks, pilings, or other objects. By extending new threads and detaching others, the mussel can move slowly from one place to another.

The scallops have developed still another form of locomotion. They open

270 BIVALVE

and close their shells with considerable force. This ejects a stream of water that causes the scallop to propel itself on a quick but erratic journey through the sea. It is the large muscle that opens and closes the shell of the scallop that is sold in the markets for food.

A few of the bivalves, such as the oyster and the shipworm, remain stationary for the greater part of their lives, finding some permanent point of attachment soon after they are born.

The boring clam, *Petricola*, is even capable of drilling holes in soft rock, such as clay or limestone, in which to live. It does this by holding on to the rock with its foot and moving the rough edges of its shell from side to side. In spite of the fact that the shell is thin, the clam slowly bores into the rock, making a hole deep enough to cover itself entirely.

The bivalves feed on microscopic plants and animals that are found in

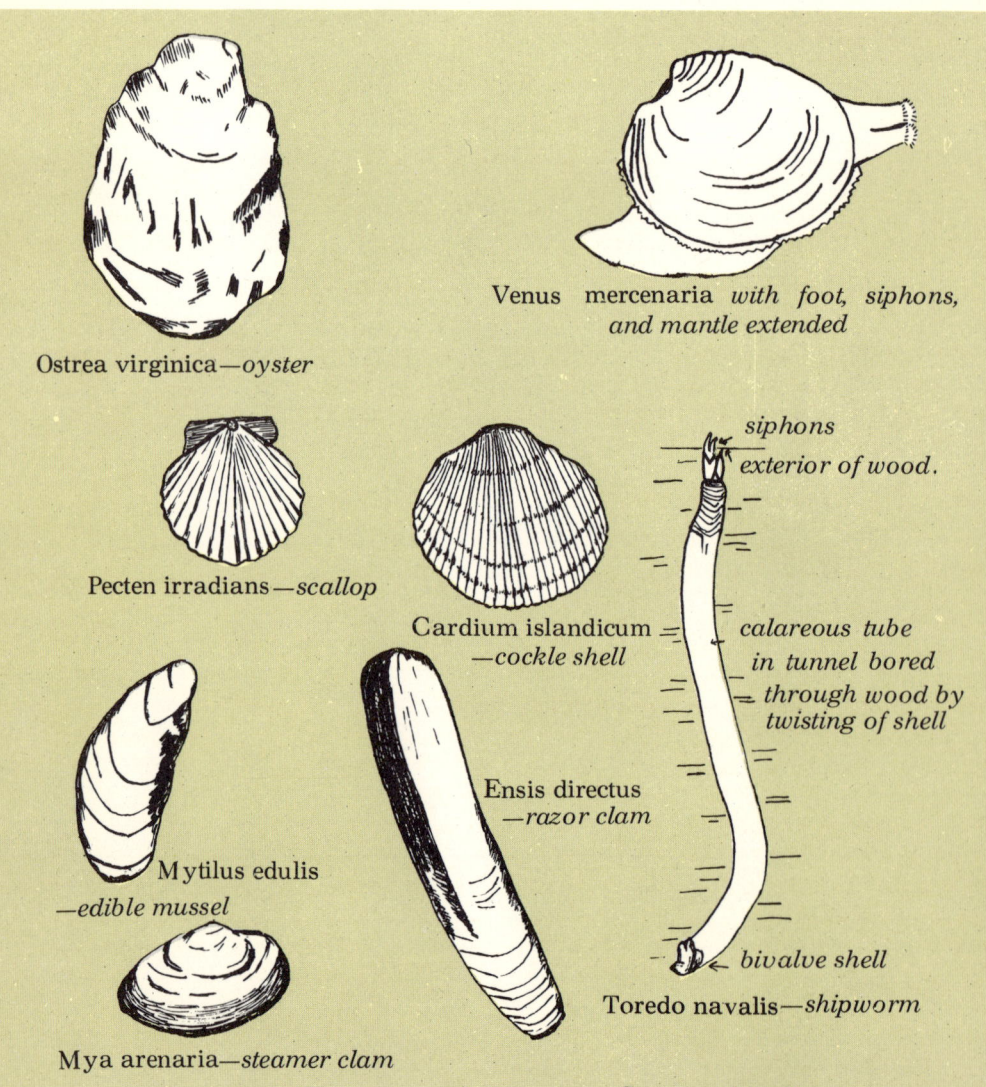

Ostrea virginica—*oyster*

Venus mercenaria *with foot, siphons, and mantle extended*

Pecten irradians—*scallop*

Cardium islandicum—*cockle shell*

siphons
exterior of wood.
calareous tube in tunnel bored through wood by twisting of shell
bivalve shell

Ensis directus—*razor clam*

Mytilus edulis—*edible mussel*

Mya arenaria—*steamer clam*

Toredo navalis—*shipworm*

Common bivalves

great abundance in the water. The edge of the mantle is fused together at one end to form two tubes or siphons. Water flows through these tubes constantly while the shell is open, one tube carrying water into the shell cavity and the other carrying water out again. This water passes over gills that absorb oxygen from the water and strain out the particles of food. It has been estimated that the average-sized clam passes three quarts of water through its siphons in the course of an hour. This ability to filter great volumes of water every few days allows shellfish to strain out almost undetectably small quantities of persistent chemical insecticides from the surrounding water and to concentrate them in their flesh to levels thousands of times greater than those found in the environment.

There are few sensory organs present, as might be expected in animals of such sedentary habits. They respond to touch and to light and have balancing organs by which they maintain their equilibrium. In some forms, such as the scallop, there is a row of pigmented eyespots along the edge of the mantle. These are sensitive to light but show no evidence of true vision.

Most bivalves have large numbers of young. An oyster may produce over half a billion eggs a year. The young are usually hatched within the body cavity of the female and then escape through the siphon into the sea. The eggs of some forms are expelled and hatch in the open water. After hatching, the young bivalves attach themselves to the fins or gills of a fish where they live as parasites for several weeks before dropping off to take up their adult existence. In a few of the freshwater clams there is no parasitic stage and the young clams pass this period in the body cavity of the female. Mortality is enormous. Many of the young provide food for other forms of life and many fail to find a proper "host." Still others fall into the mud where they suffocate. Less than one percent ever grow up.

Not only young bivalves, but the adults, too, have enemies. There is man with his clam rake and his dredges. There are the starfishes that fold their tentacles about the shells of clams and mussels and pull steadily with their hundreds of tube feet until at last the muscle holding the two halves of the shell together gives way. The starfishes then project their stomachs into the shell and consume the animal.

Polynices, the moon snail, has another method of getting into the shell. Sitting on the shell, it moves rows of rasping teeth on its tongue back and forth, thus drilling a small hole through which the soft parts of the clams may be reached. Gulls carry clams and mussels aloft and break them open by dropping them on rocks. Herons eat small bivalves of both fresh and saltwater varieties. By digging rapidly into mud or sand, clams can often elude these enemies by quickly burying themselves. The best defense of the two-shelled animals, however, is the shell itself and the strong muscle which holds it closed. This is highly protective and only the strong and per-

Exploring the seashore for some of its more interesting inhabitants

BIVALVE

sistent gain access to the soft flesh within.

Because of their popularity as food, scallops, clams, and oysters have been gathered to such an extent that in some areas they are becoming increasingly scarce. To prevent their total destruction it has become necessary to resort to both artificial propagation and legal protection. In the case of the scallop, no successful means of propagation has been found. Along the eastern coast of the United States, they are protected by a closed season during the time of breeding in the summer. In New England the soft-shelled clam is protected by laws controlling the size of clams which may be taken. No clam under two inches in length may be gathered or sold for food. It has been found that some species of clams can be farmed. This is done by reserving one-fifth of the clam bed for "seed" and harvesting each of the other fifths once in four years.

Oysters have been propagated artificially in Europe and Asia for many years. In the United States, however, the supply of oysters at first seemed inexhaustible. Later, due to overharvesting, they began to decrease rapidly. As a result, laws have been passed in many seaboard states controlling the take, and oysters for commercial use are now mostly cultivated on privately owned beds.

But the greatest destroyer of shellfish has been water pollution by oil and other industrial wastes and now, perhaps, by persistent chemical pesticides applied for mosquito control and agricultural insect pests.

In addition to serving as a human food supply, bivalves make many other contributions to man's daily living. Pearl buttons are punched from the shells of clams and oysters. Pearl for knife handles comes from the large, beautiful pearl oyster shells of the South Seas. The remains of bivalve shells of long ago, together with those of other shell animals and the corals, formed

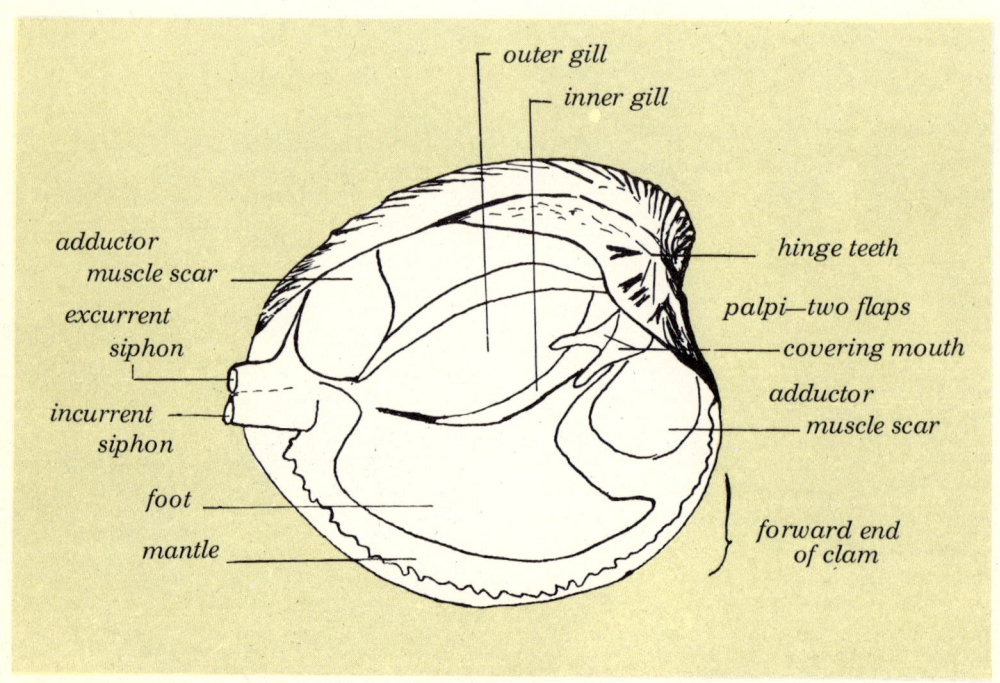

The anatomy of a typical bivalve—the clam

Starfishes are the major natural enemy of bivalves

Freshwater clam

deposits of lime on the floor of shallow seas and have since then hardened to form chalk, limestone, and marble.

Most people have ample opportunities to make the acquaintance of bivalves. Fish markets, whether inland or along the coast, usually have live oysters, scallops, and a variety of clams for sale. The animals themselves are thus easily obtainable and can be taken home for observation. A small tank of seawater is needed to watch them move about. If they are kept cool they will remain fresh for several days and the mantle, siphons, large muscle, and foot can be observed in an opened shell. Freshwater species are common in ponds, lakes, and streams, and can easily be kept in a freshwater aquarium. (See also Aquarium) —J.C.

Recommended Reading
Along the Shore—Eva L. Butler. Reynal & Hitchcock, New York.
Between the Tides—William Crowder. Dodd, Mead & Company, New York.
Field Book of Ponds and Streams—Ann H. Morgan. G. P. Putnam's Sons.
Holiday Shore—Edith M. Patch and C. L. Fenton. Macmillan Company, New York.
The Sea for Sam—W. M. Reed and W. S. Bronson. Harcourt, Brace & Company, Inc., New York.
Sea-beach at Ebb-tide—Augusta Foote Arnold. Appleton-Century Company, Inc., New York.
The Shell Book—Julia Rogers. Doubleday, Doran & Company, Inc., Garden City, New York.

BLACKBIRD
Brewer's Blackbird
Other Common Names—None
Scientific Name—*Euphagus cyanocephalus*
Family—Icteridae (troupials, blackbirds, and orioles)
Order—Passeriformes
Size—Length, eight inches
Range—Breeds from Canada south through California, Arizona, and New Mexico, and east to Minnesota, Illinois, and Kansas; recently to Michigan and Ontario. Winters from Washington and Montana south into Mexico

Brewer's blackbird walks about the lawns, gleans crumbs from the picnic benches, and flocks with the redwings about the ranches. The male is glossy black with a slight iridescence of green on the body and purple on the head and a light eye. Females are brownish-gray with dark eyes. Over most of the West Brewer's blackbirds are common wherever there is grassland with at least a few trees, in which they place stick and rootlet nests in loose or close colonies. In summer they occur even on the mountain-top meadows above timberline. The males are fearless in defense of their colonies with young swooping at, or even striking, cats and human passersby. In spring and summer the male puffs out his feathers, spreads wing and tail and sings a high, thin *kseee*.

Red-winged Blackbird
Other Common Names—Redwing, soldier bird, reed bird
Scientific Name—*Agelaius phoeniceus*
Family—Icteridae (troupials, blackbirds, and orioles)
Order—Passeriformes
Size—Length, 7½ to 9½ inches
Range—Breeds from Nova Scotia to British Columbia and south to Florida and California; winters in the South, often in large flocks, but small groups may winter in the northern, central, and northeastern United States

Nearly everyone has seen the red-

Brewer's blackbird

winged blackbird. There are other blackbirds, but none resembles it. The red-and-yellow shoulder patches of the male look like epaulets, the shoulder ornaments attached to uniforms. In some places redwings are called soldier birds, which is not a misnomer, considering the military precision with which the large flocks move about. Sometimes they gather in thousands, like vast armies, and execute skillful maneuvers as they pass over fields and uplands, every bird wheeling and turning at the same time.

In the northern part of the United States and in Canada the red-winged blackbird is a forerunner of spring, arriving with the first group of migrants—the bluebirds, robins, and meadowlarks. The very first adventurous birds often arrive in late February when the marshes are still frozen, but these are probably wanderers that have spent the winter not far away. The first real migrants do not appear until mid-March, two or more weeks later, when the marshes are flooded. These groups are made up almost entirely of adult males, and their arrival can hardly be overlooked. Every bird in the flock is singing, wheezing, or making some kind of sound.

Later in the month the flocks disband, each male taking up his station—some favorite perch from which he can watch his domain and wait for the arrival of the females, often three weeks or a month after that of the males.

The red-winged blackbird is a fearless sentinel and chases passing crows and hawks as recklessly as a kingbird. His flaming shoulder colors are displayed at every opportunity, especially when he flutters down to a cattail head or sings from a bush top. His song, a reedy, gurgling *conk-a-ree*, is pumped out with difficulty, as if it were caught in his throat. Every feather is fluffed while he sings. The female, unlike her mate, looks like a large, heavily streaked, dark sparrow.

Red-winged blackbirds nest in little groups or colonies, usually in a marsh, but sometimes in pasture or brushland. Nesting does not begin until late April or May. Somewhere among the stubble of last year's reeds, or in a bush or tussock, the nest is started. It usually takes the female about six days to build a nest but occasionally it is completed in three. The nests are seldom well made and are often crushed out of shape by the pressure of the strong new stems and reeds growing around them.

The female does all the work—the pulling of the wet sedges from the water and the weaving of them into the nest. Although the male offers no help, he displays much interest and seems to offer encouragement. The three or four eggs are typical of the blackbird-oriole family—pale bluish-white with dark scratches and scrawls on the large end as if the female had come to the nest with ink on her feet. The red-skinned young are hatched after fourteen days

Red-winged blackbird

of incubation. After 12 days of feeding they are ready to leave the nest. While the young are being raised the usual blackbird diet of weed seeds changes largely to a diet of insects. They are especially fond of cankerworms and will fly a considerable distance from the marsh to get them.

In the southern United States redwings are year-round residents; the summer birds are later joined by winter flocks from the North.

Studies of winter roosts of mixed blackbirds during the 1960's revealed the existence of a score of roosts with a million or more birds in them. Most of these roosts are mixed populations including starlings, grackles, and cowbirds, all of them blackbirds in the loose sense of the word. These large winter roosts are not new, however, and it should not be assumed, from them, that blackbirds are increasing in numbers. (*See Cowbird and Starling*) —A.H-B, Jr.

Rusty Blackbird
Other Common Names—Rusty grackle, thrush blackbird
Scientific Name—*Euphagus carolinus*
Family—Icteridae (troupials, blackbirds, and orioles)
Order—Passeriformes
Size—Length, 9½ inches
Range—Eastern and northern North America. Breeds from Alaska and northern Mackenzie south to central Ontario and northern New England. Winters mainly south of the Ohio and Delaware river valleys to Gulf Coast

This species, otherwise called rusty grackle and thrush blackbird, is perhaps less known to the average bird student than any other member of the family. This, perhaps, is due to its shy and retiring habits, together with the fact that its breeding range is mostly beyond the usual haunts of man. The male, moreover, may sometimes be confused in the field with the grackles.

The rusty blackbird is more aquatic

Rusty blackbirds, male in spring (front); and female in fall (rear)

than any of its relatives; it often may be found feeding in shallow water, where it picks up the larvae of insects, small crustaceans, and other forms of life. As if further to accentuate its aquatic habits, the common call note, *chuck*, so closely resembles that of the wood frogs that inhabit its favorite haunts that it is often difficult, at a distance, to distinguish between the notes. Like redwings, flocks of these birds assemble in treetops and engage in a musical chorus that is quite unlike the vocal performance of any other bird.

The nest is of twigs, grasses, or mosses, usually in thickets of conifers, in swamps or near borders of lakes or streams. From four to seven pale green eggs, thickly blotched with light and dark brown, are laid.

Yellow-headed blackbirds, male (above); female (below)

Yellow-headed Blackbird
Other Common Names—Yellowhead
Scientific Name—*Xanthocephalus xanthocephalus*
Family—Icteridae (troupials, blackbirds, and orioles)
Order—Passeriformes
Size—Length, 10 inches
Range—Breeds from British Columbia to the Saskatchewan Valley, south through the Central Plains to Arkansas, and west to southern California. Winters in northern and central Mexico; a few in a southern strip from California to Louisiana. Infrequently, a rare straggler appears in the East

The yellow-headed blackbird is predominantly a native of the Great Plains. In some parts of its range it invades regions not strictly prairie, yet it still belongs, by right, to the vast, treeless plains of the interior and to the sparsely wooded areas immediately to the east and west.

One invariable condition is necessary to induce this bird to establish a summer residence—an abundant and permanent water supply with the kind of plantlife suited to its rather particular tastes. Preference is usually given to a swamp or slough that is wet and has open water, never to meadows or marshes that are merely damp and subject to drying out. The tule beds of the valleys of the Rocky Mountains, the quill-reed brakes of the North, and the flag swamps of the South are acceptable to the yellow-headed blackbird as nesting places.

The yellowhead breeds in colonies which are often of vast proportions. It is loyal to its homesite and returns year after year, deserting it only with the drying up of the marsh. The yellowhead is closely restricted to its special nesting haunts. In the spring the members of each colony go directly to their particular territory, seldom wandering into the surrounding countryside before completion of the breeding period.

In the northward movement in spring, the vanguard of the yellowheads that are to breed in Canada reach the international boundary about the beginning of May, the males preceding the females by a few days. In Minnesota, stragglers enter the southern part of the state the middle of April, but it is not until the end of April or early in May that they become numerous. The song of the yellowhead is remarkably unmusical. It is a low, hoarse *krick* or *krack* that terminates in a rasping squeal, seemingly produced with much effort.

In the Minnesota region they nest almost exclusively in the dense growth of quill-reeds, which fills or encircles many of the sloughs and shallow lakes of the prairie and semi-prairie parts of the state. Occasionally, spring freshets or other disturbances may drive them to place their nests among bulrushes in upland sloughs, or, more rarely still, in willows and bushes adjacent to open water. Nest building usually begins in central Minnesota about the middle of May and continues well into June. It seems probable, however, that only one brood is raised in a season, the great variation in the nesting time being due to depredations by various small animals, which devour the eggs and young, and to severe climatic disturbances.

The female builds the nest and incubates the eggs without any assistance from the male. The male assists in caring for the young, especially after they leave the nest. Usually three to five eggs are laid a day apart. They vary from almost elliptical to pronounced ovate, and lengths and widths also vary. The shell is smooth and glossy. The color varies from a soiled grayish-white to a pale olive-white, and in rare instances has a faint pink-lilac hue. The usual period of incubation is 10 days. The young remain in the nest about 12 days. Yellowheads eat angleworms, insects, the white grubs of the June beetle, grasshoppers, waste seeds and grains.

When the nesting season is over, old and young yellowheads leave the sloughs and marshes and congregate in straggling flocks, sometimes accompanied by red-winged blackbirds and grackles. Their southward movement begins early, often ending by the first of September.
—A.B., Jr.

BLACK CANYON OF THE GUNNISON NATIONAL MONUMENT

Location—Western Colorado
Size—22 square miles
Mammals—Bighorn sheep, mule deer, elk, bears, badgers, marmots, porcupines
Birdlife—Red-tailed hawks, sparrow hawks, golden eagles, blue grouse, white-throated swifts, broad-tailed hummingbirds, violet-green swallows, Steller's jays, American magpies, mountain chickadees, mountain bluebirds
Plants—Pinyons, junipers, scrub oaks, mountain mahogany, mock oranges

The rock through which the Gunnison River has cut its course is among the oldest on earth, dating back to the pre-Cambrian period (*See Geological Periods*). The greatest depth of the gorge is 2,425 feet; at one point, the two opposite rims of the gorge are only 1,300 feet apart. The monument is also noted for bighorn sheep and for the ancientness of the pinyons (pines), some of which are 750 years old.

Accommodations—Two campgrounds within the park; other overnight facilities available in Montrose, Colorado
Headquarters—Mesa Verde National Park, Colorado
—G.B.S.

Black-eyed susans

BLACK-EYED SUSAN
Other Common Names—Brown-eyed susan
Scientific Name—*Rudbeckia serotina*
Family—Compositae (composite family)
Range—Throughout the eastern United States and Canada
Habitat—Fields and waste places
Time of Blooming—May to first frost

As the lands in the eastern United States were brought under cultivation, this plant spread eastward from the prairies and plains. It is said that the pretty weed made its way to the East in the clover seeds from western fields. A biennial species, it is now very common in the eastern United States. It is the state flower of Maryland.

The black-eyed susan belongs to a group called, generally, coneflowers. The tiny tubular flowers in the center of a flower head are arranged horizontally. Ten to twenty ray flowers surround, and are attached to a chocolate-brown, cone-shaped disk in the center of the flower head. The rays are a brilliant yellow while the tiny tubular flowers are purple. The whole plant is rough and hairy and grows from one to two feet high.

The leaves on the lower part of the stem are broad and three-ribbed; the upper ones are narrower and lance-shaped. The stem and leaves are quite rigid and covered with stiff hairs, which, if brushed against, may irritate the skin.

The black-eyed susan is well endowed with a flower structure that assures the fertilization of its seed-producing ovules. Its long anthers unite into a tube whose base closely surrounds the pistils. At the top of the tube are two hairy filaments that brush the pollen into the tube as it grows upward. The filaments stand above the rest of the flower like antennae, in perfect position to dust visiting insects. The nectar, contained in the deep tubular brown florets, may be drained only by long, slender tongues; however, the pollen is accessible to all, and the black-eyed susan is visited by numerous insects.

The black-eyed susan is a member of the family Compositae, the largest and most advanced family of flowering plants. The composites contain about one-tenth of all known species of flowering plants, one-eighth of which are indigenous to North America. Plants of this family are often characterized by flowers that are crowded closely together to form a flat head.

The black-eyed susan abounds in meadows, pastures, and along roadsides, making a brilliant show of color. Despite its beauty, the black-eyed susan is disliked by some farmers. An aggressive plant, it is difficult to eradicate once it has established itself in pastures and fields. On the other hand, the black-eyed susan is a valuable pioneering plant on bare, eroded soil. Because it will grow on barren places, it will hold the soil in place until other plants can get a start. —A.M.M.

BLACKWATER NATIONAL WILDLIFE REFUGE

Location — Eastern Maryland
Size — 17 square miles
Mammals — Muskrats, raccoons, rabbits
Birdlife — In summer, bobwhites, rails, gallinules, warblers; in winter, Canada geese, pintail ducks, shovellers, hooded mergansers, gadwalls, black ducks, teals, and widgeons; all year, bald eagles, pileated woodpeckers, brown-headed nuthatches

The refuge was established to provide a stopover point for migrating geese and ducks, and thousands of each of the more common species can be found there at the same time. Roads and footpaths extend throughout the tidal marshes, freshwater ponds, croplands, and stands of loblolly pines within the refuge. A considerable acreage is planted to crops on which the birds feed.

Accommodations — Available in Cambridge
Headquarters — In the refuge; Route 1, Cambridge, Maryland

Hooded mergansers can be seen at Blackwater National Wildlife Refuge, Maryland. (From Audubon's Elephant Folio)

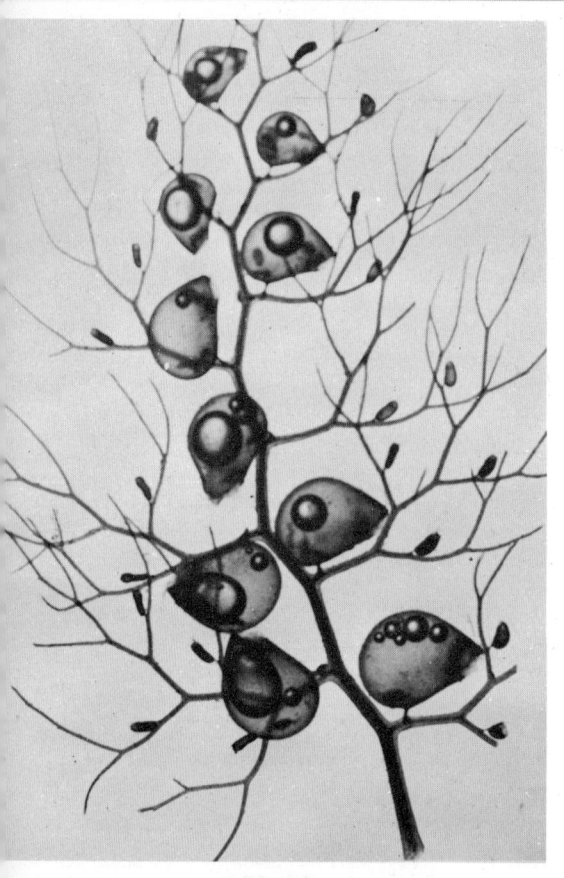

Bladderwort

BLADDERWORT

Few plants are carnivorous (meat-eating), but the bladderworts are, along with the pitcher plants, and sundews. They are the order Polemoniales; family Lentibulariaceae. Most of them are rootless, floating plants of freshwater ponds, but a few grow in moist soil. The floating ones have a mat of finely dissected leaves a few inches under the surface of the water. The leaves are edged with tiny sacs, requiring magnification to be studied. These are really traps, and ordinarily the sacs, or bladders, are shrunken and empty. Should a tiny aquatic animal brush against a guard hair at the mouth of the bladder, the watertight door springs open, and the animal is sucked inside. Digestive juices and bacteria of the bladderworts reduce the ingested animal to compounds that can be assimilated by the plant.

Bladderworts are flowering plants with yellow, pink, or purple blossoms. About 230 species are known from all over the world, and 14 are native to the United States and Canada. —G.B.S.

BLOODROOT

Other Common Names—Redroot, Indian paint
Scientific Name—*Sanguinaria canadensis*
Family—Papaveraceae (poppy family)
Range—Nova Scotia to Nebraska, south to Florida and Arkansas
Habitat—Woods rich in humus
Time of Blooming—April and May

The dainty waxy, white flower, which is sometimes one and one-half inches across, has 4 to 12 petals and 2 sepals that usually drop as soon as the flower opens. Four of the petals are slightly narrower than the others and grow alternately among the larger, broader petals. This gives the flower a somewhat square appearance.

On a sunny morning the blossoms will open wide. In the afternoon they begin to rise and by nightfall they will have closed completely; they also close during stormy weather, thus protecting the inner parts of the flower from the rain and cold.

No nectar is produced by the flowers until the stamens mature. Nevertheless, honeybees and bumblebees are attracted to the frail white flower as soon as the pistil matures and, if the bee has already been in contact with an older flower, cross-fertilization occurs.

The thick rootstock of the bloodroot enables it to store food under ground during the winter. Because of this available food supply the plants bloom earlier in the year than fibrous-rooted plants that must manufacture food in the spring in preparation for blooming. The bloodroot blooms while the trees are leafless and sunlight penetrates to the forest floor.

During early April the flower bud, rolled in a basal leaf, emerges from the protective rootstock. John Burroughs likened the bud to a papoose rolled in a blanket. The single leaf has three to seven deep lobes and is blue-green in color.

The orange-red juice of this plant is responsible for its name. It contains an alkaloid that if eaten affects the nervous system and muscles of the body. Indians used it as a dye to paint their faces.

The bloodroot is a member of the poppy family. Pollination is generally performed by bees, and the resulting fruit is usually a one-celled capsule. Other members of the poppy family include the celandine and wood poppy, and the well-known California poppy of the West. —A.M.M.

Bloodroot

BLUEBIRD
Eastern Bluebird
Other Common Names—Blue Robin, blue red-breast, Wilson's bluebird
Scientific Name—*Sialia sialis*
Family—Turdidae (thrushes, solitaires, and bluebirds)
Order—Passeriformes
Size—Length, 6½ to 7½ inches
Range—Breeds from Newfoundland to southern Saskatchewan and south to Texas and Florida. Winters mainly in southern United States. A few brave the winters of southern New England, New York, Michigan, Minnesota, and South Dakota

The bluebird is the state bird of Missouri and New York. Its cheerful *chur-wi* is a sign that spring is near. There are two other birds that are mostly blue—the blue jay and the indigo bunting. The bluebird is the only one with a reddish breast and, with its blue back and white belly, it carries the colors of the American flag. Henry David Thoreau observed that it carries the sky on its back; John Burroughs added, and the earth on its breast.

Bluebirds were probably more common in the cities at one time than they are now. In the 1870's, house sparrows were gaining a foothold in the United States. They contested bluebirds for the right to live near the buildings in the towns. The sparrows, being nonmigratory, were well established in these quarters when bluebirds returned from the South. There was nothing for them to do but move into the country.

This gentle bird is now faced with another problem — the starling — also brought over from Europe. There is competition for both food and nesting sites. Bluebirds depend on berry-bearing trees, shrubs, and vines to tide them over when late snowstorms cover the ground early in spring. However, a roving flock of starlings in winter can clean out a mountain ash tree in a few hours. Nothing is left for the needy spring travelers.

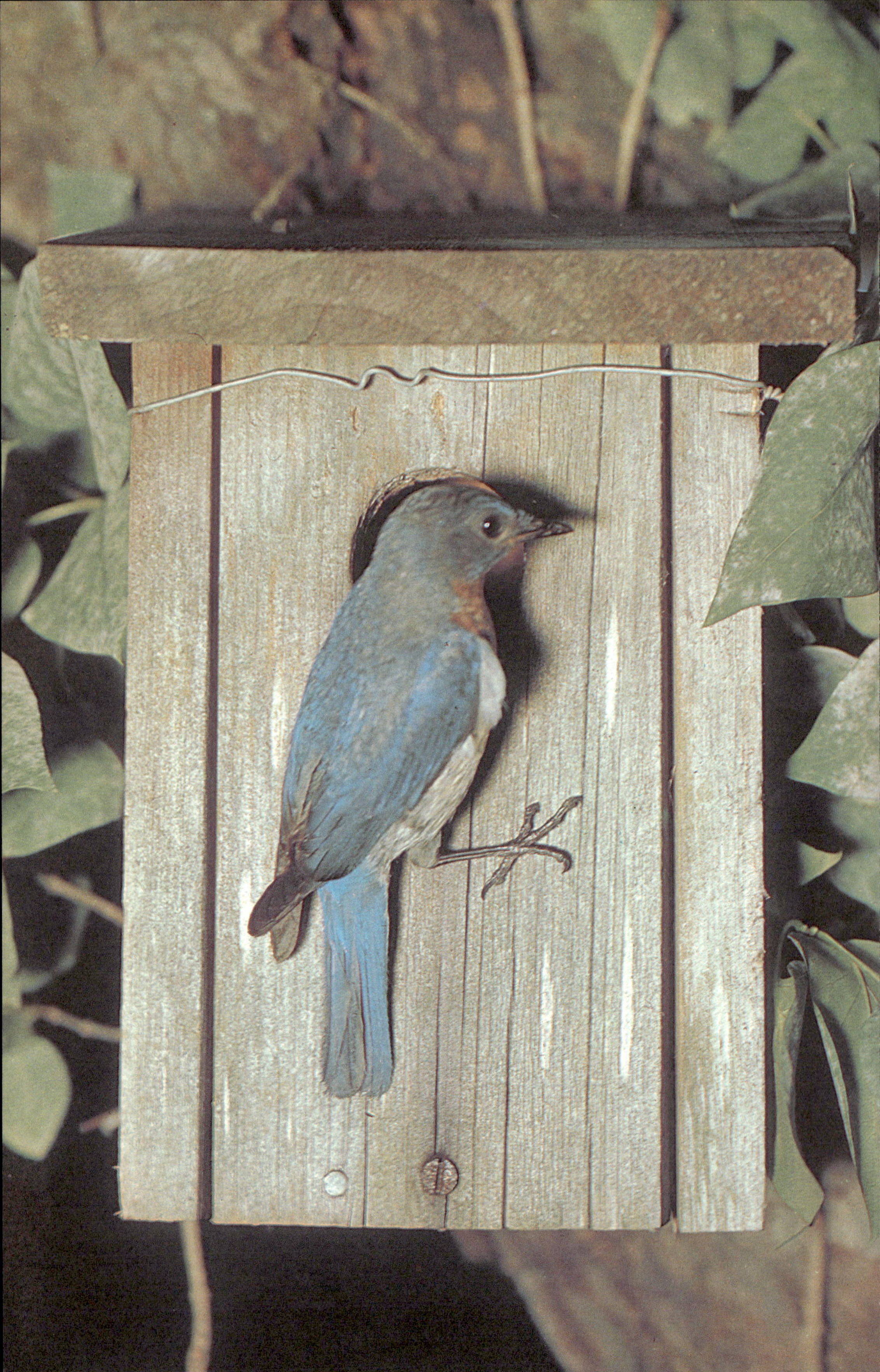

Among the bluebird's favorite haunts are old apple and pear orchards that are in a state of decay. The holes and cavities in the trees afford ideal nesting sites. If these are lacking, a hole in a rail or post, or a cozy birdbox supplies its needs. A starling cannot enter a hole with a diameter smaller than two inches. An inch-and-a-half entrance will accommodate a bluebird nicely. This is important to observe when building a house specifically for the bluebird. Bluebirds line the interior of their houses with grasses and pine needles. Four or five eggs, pale blue in color, are laid, that take about 14 days to hatch.

Two broods are usually raised. The female does most, if not all, of the incubating of the eggs. At first the young are fed insects. Approximately two-thirds of the bluebird's food consists of insects —beetles, grasshoppers, and caterpillars; the other third is largely wild fruit.

In their first plumage, young bluebirds are speckled, showing a definite resemblance to their close relatives, the thrushes. Both robins and bluebirds are thrushes, but it is only in their juvenile plumage that this relationship is plainly revealed.

Most bluebirds spend the winter in small flocks in the southern part of the United States, but a few attempt to winter as far north as southern New England and South Dakota. In coastal areas they mingle with myrtle warblers, sitting hunch-shouldered on the telegraph wires or wandering in little groups among the bayberry bushes. A frugal fare of berries is all the frigid north has to offer in December. —A.B., Jr.

Western Bluebird
Other Common Names—California bluebird
Scientific Name—*Sialia mexicana*
Family—Turdidae (thrushes, solitaires, and bluebirds)
Order—Passeriformes
Size—Length, seven inches

Range—Breeds throughout Pacific states and east to northern Idaho and western Montana, and south in Rocky Mountain section through Colorado and Utah to Mexico, southern Utah, and western Texas

The western bluebird is easily distinguished from its eastern counterpart by the chestnut color on its back, its blue throat, and generally darker blue color. In the East a bluebird might follow the melting snows for several hundred miles to reach its summer New England home, whereas a migrating western bluebird in many parts of the West has merely to climb the nearest range of mountains. This relatively short journey from the valleys where it spends the winter to the yellow pine belt where it nests is often called vertical migration. Another bluebird, the mountain bluebird which is turquoise blue above and below, also lives at higher altitudes in some of the western ranges.

The calls of the western bluebird are a hard chattering note, and a short *pew* or *mew*. —A.B., Jr.

Western bluebird

Eastern bluebirds

Bluefish

BLUEFISH
Other Common Names — Skipjack, snapper
Scientific Name — *Pomatomus saltatrix*
Family — Pomatomidae (bluefishes)
Order — Perciformes
Size — Length, to 4 feet, weight to 30 pounds
Range — Irregularly distributed in warmer seas. In the western Atlantic Ocean from Argentina to Cape Cod; some as far north as Nova Scotia

The bluefish is the only member of its family. It has a moderately stout body (about one-quarter as deep as it is long). The bluefish snout is moderately pointed and its mouth is large and oblique with a projecting lower jaw. Both jaws are ringed with a single series of strong, cone-shaped teeth. The teeth are one-eighth to one-quarter of an inch long in a specimen that weighs about 10 pounds.

The bluefish has two dorsal fins. The front dorsal fin is composed of seven or eight connected spines and is shaped like a small low crescent. The rear dorsal fin lies directly behind and has 23 to 26 rays — more than twice the length of and about twice as high as the front dorsal fin. It descends gradually as it runs backward almost to the fish's tail. The anal fin is similar in shape and length to the rear dorsal fin.

The fish's back and upper sides have a greenish hue; the belly and lower sides are silvery. The pectoral fin has a black notch at its base.

Bluefishes are swift swimmers and perhaps the most vicious fishes in the sea. They travel in dense schools attacking and eating other fishes. They will kill great numbers of schooling fishes, eating only the part of each fish that they get with the first bite and then moving on to tear at another.

Bluefishes are an excellent food fish. They are taken extensively by game fishermen and commercial fisheries but their abundance varies greatly from year to year. Young bluefishes are called snappers.
— M.R.

BLUE FLAG
Other Common Names — Water flag, fleur-de-lis
Scientific Name — *Iris versicolor*
Family — Iridaceae (iris family)
Range — Across northern United States south to Florida
Habitat — Open marshy areas
Time of Blooming — May through August

The blue flag belongs to the iris family, which has over a thousand members. The first part of its scientific name, *Iris*, is the Greek word for rainbow — an appropriate description for a flower that is so variegated in color. In general, the irises are known as flags, since the *Iris germanica* served as the model for various flags and banners. The term fleur-de-lis is a time-honored corruption of flower-of-Louis, after Louis VII of France who used an iris as his symbol.

This beautiful and familiar flower grows from a thickened rootstalk and has stemless, flat, and arrow-shaped leaves. The flower buds open one by one at the top of the stalk, which grows from one to two and one-half feet high. The sepals are very large and showy and resemble flower petals.

The conspicuous color of this flower

Blue flag

assures its cross-pollination by attracting many insects. The position of the stamens is such that they cannot reach the stigma, thus safeguarding the blue flag against self-fertilization.

The blue flag seems to be especially designed to attract bees. Its three broad branches and sepals form a tunnel-like thoroughfare for the coming and going of this insect. The three sections of the style are wide and lie flat against the purple-lined sepals and cover the stamens so closely that a bee seeking nectar can scarcely avoid getting pollen on its back. The deep purple stripes found on the true petals of the flower, some believe, are an aid to the bee in acting as a color guide that indicates the direction of the honey wells. —A.M.M.

BLUET

Other Common Names—Quaker-ladies
Scientific Name—*Houstonia caerulea*
Family—Rubiaceae (madder family)
Range—Nova Scotia to Quebec, south to Georgia and Missouri
Habitat—Open grassy fields
Time of Blooming—April through July

This dainty blue or lavender flower often forms such large colonies in moist fields they give the appearance of a blue carpet. It is a favorite spring flower.

The tiny four-parted flower is tubular with a yellow center and is seldom over one-half inch in diameter. Usually two flowers blossom at the top of the slender stem, each on separate branches that are joined together in a thin tube at the base. In the budding flower the four lobes of the corolla are vertical and form a protective sheath for the more delicate inner parts. These lobes are more horizontal in the open flower.

Leaves grow from a basal rosette and tiny opposite leaves are on the stem. Each leaf is smooth-edged and has one vein extending to the tip.

Bluets bloom early in the spring before the grass has reached much height, and finish producing seeds before the grass overtops them and shuts off their light.

Bluets are among the flowers botanically termed *dimorphous*, that is, occurring in two forms. This refers to the size and position of the stamens and pistils, some of which have tall pistils and short stamens, while others have short pistils and tall stamens. The two forms are a clever arrangement for cross-pollination and insure the plant almost completely against self-fertilization. In one form the stigmas are protruding and the four anthers are attached to the tube about halfway down. In a second form the anthers are located at the base of the flower. Thus, an insect can proceed either from the center to the base or from the base to the center. Cross-polli-

Bluets

nation in these plants is generally performed by butterflies and bees.

Some members of the madder family, such as coffee, cinchona (from which quinine is derived), and madder (the source of a brilliant red dye), are important commercial plants. Some familiar but less important plants belonging to this family are partridgeberry, the bedstraws, and the buttonbush that grows beside streams and freshwater ponds.

There are some 25 species of the genus Houstonia (named for botanist William Houston) in the world. They are all natives of Mexico, the United States, or Canada. Thymeleaf bluets live on the slopes along the Blue Ridge and Appalachian mountains from Georgia to Pennsylvania. The star violet, another bluet, lives on the dry plains of the central United States, and the least bluet colonizes dry hillsides of similar range.

—A.M.M.

BOBCAT
Other Common Names—Bay lynx, wildcat
Scientific Name—*Lynx rufus*
Family—Felidae (cats)
Order—Carnivora
Size—Male: body length, 30 to 40 inches; tail, 4 to 6½ inches; height at shoulder, 20 to 23 inches; weight, 12 to 25, or rarely, to 40 pounds. Females smaller
Range—Extreme southern Canada and Nova Scotia, south throughout the entire United States and into Mexico

The bobcat, smaller and lighter than the related lynx, has shorter whiskers and smaller feet than its northern cousin. It also prefers a different type of country, inhabiting brushlands, scrub, and thickets rather than the deep woods preferred by the lynx.

Bobcats feed on mice, rabbits, muskrats, squirrels, and, occasionally, on birds. They often live near human settlements and sometimes raid domestic poultry houses. Their hunting technique is similar to that of the house cat — they slink through cover to pounce on their prey in a sudden burst of speed.

The color of the short, dense fur varies according to the region. In the deserts it is gray or buff-colored and overlaid with light streaks and spots. In mountainous, wooded country the fur is often reddish, with very dark markings.

Bobcats live alone, except for a brief pairing in midwinter. The females have from one to four kittens in early spring. The kittens are born and raised in dens in hollow trees, caves, or in deep thickets. The male takes no part in raising the young.

—G.B.S.

Recommended Reading

The Bobcat of North America—Stanley P. Young. Stackpole and Company, Harrisburg, Pennsylvania.
World of the Bobcat—Joe Van Wormer. J. B. Lippincott Company. Philadelphia.

The bobcat is an expert climber

BOBOLINK

Other Common Names—Ricebird, reedbird
Scientific Name—*Dolichonyx oryzivorus*
Family—Icteridae (troupials, blackbirds, and orioles)
Order—Passeriformes
Size—Length, eight inches
Range—Breeds from southern British Columbia, Saskatchewan, and Nova Scotia, south to northeastern California, Colorado, northern Missouri, Indiana, and Maryland. Winters in South America and northern Argentina

Bobolink is a familiar name even to those who have never seen one, for it appears frequently in song and story.

Perhaps the song of the bobolink is what endears it most to man. During the mating and nesting season, from early May to early July, the male's bubbling notes can be heard in the meadows of the northern United States and southern Canada. This song begins on a low key and goes rollicking joyously upward and has a slightly metallic quality. The male sings to proclaim his territory and to woo his mate.

The male arrives in Florida in mid-April, ahead of the female. He has flown along the bobolink's ancestral migration route from South America, sometimes a distance of 6,800 miles. His nuptial plumage, which he acquired in late winter, is hidden beneath long, buffy feather tips. By the time he reaches Florida, the buffy feather tips have worn away and he is totally different in appearance from when he started out. Now he is black and white on top, with a little yellow skullcap, and dark underneath. The male bobolink is the only American songbird that is light above and dark below during the nesting season. The appearance of the female is the same all year round—a buffy-gray with stripes on her head, looking somewhat like a large sparrow.

The nest is usually in a little depression in the ground, cleverly concealed at the foot of a clump of grass or clover.

Bobolinks, male (above); female (below)

The four to seven blotched eggs vary a great deal; sometimes the ground-color is pale gray, dull bluish, or even rusty-brown. They hatch after 10 days of brooding by the female.

The young bobolinks grow rapidly on an insect diet and, like many other ground-nesting birds, leave the nest before they are really ready to fly.

By mid-July the nestlings are on their own sufficiently to evade man's mowing or harvesting machines as men come to reap the seeds of grains and grasses. As man's agricultural activities have moved westward, so has the bobolink and it now lives even as far west as Washington and Oregon.

With the coming of mid- and late summer, bobolinks gather by the thousands from British Columbia to Massachusetts to start on the long trip back to South America. Bobolinks nesting in British Columbia and the western part

Migration route of the bobolink

of the United States do not take the southerly or most direct route as the typical migrating western bird does but travel a southeasterly route to Florida from where they start their long journey to their winter quarters.

By now the male has lost his handsome plumage and is buffy and olive like the female and the young.

As they fly their cry is a *Pink* or *Tink*, a familiar sound to most birdwatchers. In former years, as they passed through the Carolinas and Georgia the bobolinks feasted in ricefields to the dismay of the farmers. Known as ricebirds or reedbirds, because of their depredations they were killed by the thousands and sold for food. Now the bobolink, as a songbird, is protected by law.

From Florida the bobolinks make the long flight to Central and South America and remain there until the cycle begins anew with the spring migration northward. —B.D.

BOBWHITE

Other Common Names—Bobwhite quail
Scientific Name—*Colinus virginianus*
Family—Phasianidae (quails, pheasants, peacocks)
Order—Galliformes
Size—Length, 10½ inches
Range—East of the Rocky Mountains, roughly south of a line drawn from southern Wyoming to Massachusetts, and extending into Mexico

The bobwhite, a small, reddish, chickenlike bird, is the state bird of Oklahoma

In addition to the familiar loud and cheery calls, *bob-white* and *poor bob-white*, that anyone who can whistle can imitate, this bird has a rallying call it uses to regroup the covey after it has been scattered. It is a mellow-whistled *ka-loi-kee, ka-loi-kee.*

Bobwhites like open fields, weedy places, and woodland borders. As the little flock wanders about, the birds chatter in low tones. Now and then some unusual sound causes them to squat or to stand rigidly still. In a few moments, if no danger threatens, they relax and continue on their way.

Most of their travels are on foot; they do not use their short, rounded wings except in quick bursts of flight when frightened. To exercise their wings, bobwhites on the ground frequently stretch upward and *whir* their wings. When evening comes the little flock roosts on the ground, squatting in a circle with tails pointing toward the center and heads facing out. This not only conserves the heat of their bodies during cold weather but if some wandering animal should discover them in the night they can scatter in all directions like an exploding bombshell.

When the warm days of spring come, male bobwhites, which had been peaceable companions all winter, become irritable with each other. They puff themselves up and make threatening rushes toward possible rivals for the brown hens.

In the South, nests of bobwhite have

Bobwhites are hardy birds that survive harsh winter by huddling close together

been recorded during almost every month of the year, but most are found between April and October. In southern New England the nesting season is much shorter. Almost 9 out of every 10 nests are in the dead, weedy growth of the year before. Rarely are they found in new grass. On farms where fires are set to remove the ground growth, bobwhites soon disappear.

Apparently, the male does all the nest building while his mate watches, but they are so shy that very few naturalists have ever seen the actual act of building the nest. The hollow nest is lined with straws and is usually roofed over. Sometimes several nests are built if the first nest is not satisfactory. The white eggs are laid one a day until there are 14 or 15. It is rare for a nest to have as few as 7 or 8 eggs, and nests have been found with as many as 42 eggs in them but these are presumed to be the combined efforts of several birds and are always failures.

It is not until the last egg is laid that incubation actually starts. The young all hatch within an hour of each other at the end of 22 or 23 days of incubation. Even if the last few eggs have not hatched the young birds leave in a short while as they are precocial, or "nest-quitters," at an early age.

The newly hatched young are wet, miserable-looking things at first but they soon dry out into fluffy chicks hardly larger than one's thumb. Their protection relies much on their brown coloration as they squat silently among the dead leaves and brown earth when danger threatens. Dangers are many, too, not only from cats and other animals, but also from accidents, diseases, parasites, and storms. They all take their toll. It is easy for one to see why such a large number of eggs is necessary to assure the bobwhite a secure place on this earth.

The number of eggs a bird lays is suggestive of the number of natural enemies it has. A certain number of young must be raised to take care of losses until the next nesting season. Nature thus strives to keep each kind of bird in balance. If two quail lay 16 eggs, there are usually only two young left the following year — 14 have perished in the meantime. Some of the eggs may have been eaten by ground prowlers; the chicks may be caught by snakes, cats, or foxes; and the adults themselves may be caught sometimes. However, the species has lived with its natural enemies for centuries and has survived. It is only when the environment in which they live is changed, or when they are hunted too relentlessly by man, that quail disappear.

The chicks are so tiny at first that they are not much bigger than large grasshoppers. But their wings develop so early that they can actually fly by the time they are half grown. At 15 weeks they resemble their parents.

In early fall bobwhites often join together to form large groups called coveys. By then the sharp-shinned hawk and Cooper's hawk are migrating south and the quail, to protect themselves from these predatory birds, must stay closer to cover than before. The leaves of trees and shrubs are thinning and by the time the hunting season opens it is much harder for quail to remain hidden. When at last the hunters and their dogs appear, the coveys scatter in wild confusion. By the end of the season many coveys have been greatly reduced and the remnants often join together to form new coveys.

In some states the bobwhite is protected, in others, it is so numerous that states allow it to be hunted as a gamebird. If it is not hunted too relentlessly it is able to maintain a fairly stable population.

In the North the winter is the most critical time in the bobwhite's life. If a flock of 20 quail begins the winter on a farm on which the food and plant cover will support only 12, at least 8 are sure to perish. If one wishes to have more quail, raising them and then releasing them is not the answer. As with most other birds, food and cover are the most important factors for survival. There is an old belief that quail get along best on farms, but intensive modern farming methods can drive them out completely. On the other hand, most soil conservation efforts and attempts to check erosion by planting clover increase the number of quail.

About one-seventh of the bobwhite's food is made up of insects, the other six-sevenths of vegetable matter—seeds of grasses, sedges, weeds, and especially leguminous plants such as clover. It is thus evident why farms that have been "cleaned up" too much by cutting off weeds and other cover cannot support bobwhites.

As far as is known, bobwhites never migrate and they rarely wander more than two or three miles from the place where they were hatched. Many of them stay within a quarter of a mile of one spot the year around. —A.B.Jr.

BOG

A bog is wet, spongy ground, an inadequately drained area rich in plant residues. It is usually acid in reaction, and the low-growing water plants of the bog surround and encroach on quiet open waters such as a pond. Bogs are usually the forerunners of a swamp (*See under Swamp*) as they extend outward with their plant cover, engulfing the pond slowly but surely in their march into and over the pond waters. There they build a mat of plants that grows deeper and deeper each year. As it thickens on the water, it becomes a seedbed for shrubs and finally for trees. The plants of the bog are a changing or modifying plant association known as *pioneers*. They are the first plants on the water, and if they are allowed to grow, unchecked, will eventually convert the pond into a swamp. —J.K.T.

The Composition of a Bog

In Alaska, Canada, and in the northern and eastern United States, poorly drained wet areas, called bogs, are often dominated by a spongy mat of vegetation. The dominant plant in these boggy places is usually the sphagnum moss, a rootless plant that can continue to grow year after year, even in open water.

The sphagnum's ability to grow without roots allows it to extend its mat outward from the shore of a pond and gradually cover its surface. Because the

Cranberry Swamp, Pennsylvania

stem of the plant dies or breaks off after it has grown hardly a foot long, the mat is at first quite shallow. But as the moss continues to grow at its tip, the mat thickens. Gradually, other plants, especially northern members of the blueberry family — small shrubs such as leatherleaf and bog rosemary — become established on the mat. Their interlocking roots will so strengthen it that soon the mat is firm enough to support a man's weight. But for many years afterward this floating mat will undulate under one's weight, hence the familiar term, *quaking bog*.

The famous *peat bogs* of Ireland and Scandinavia are of this type, but most of them are thicker and firmer than similar bogs in most of North America. This is because they have grown faster. Bogs grow best in cool, wet climate. They prosper in regions that are warm enough to foster the growth of their chief plant, the sphagnum moss, but yet cool enough to slow the activity of the many bacteria that quickly decompose vegetation in warmer areas. Furthermore, the chemistry of sphagum moss soon makes the environment in which it grows acid, and this too inhibits decomposition. The oldest recovered human flesh is that of Danes who drowned in the Tollund bog of Denmark 2,000 years ago. Their bodies were preserved intact in the cool, acid environment of the bog all these 20 centuries.

Sphagnum bogs that still occur are icts of the Ice Age that dominated so much of Canada and the northern United States until about 10,000 years ago. Throughout the northern tier of states, and down the Appalachian Mountains at increasing elevations the farther south one goes, small relict bogs may be found in the hollows of the hills.

Many of these southern bogs are the homes of such northern trees as tamarack and black spruce, species that are now found only at lower elevations in cold regions. They have persisted because the bogs remain colder than the surrounding uplands now grown to oak, hickory, and maple. Not only has the flow of cold air into these bogs helped to lower their average annual temperatures, but ice that forms under the sphagnum moss is sheltered from the sun until well into late spring. This helps furnish that cool climate the spruce and larch need to persist.

–R.C.C.

Where to Visit a Bog

There is something so magical and so alluring about northern plants and animals that few naturalists can resist exploring a cold northern bog. When one thinks of a trip for boreal plants and animals, one may envision a northward trek, or one that would lead inland, in the eastern United States, ascending the higher peaks of the southern Appalachians. It is not necessary to climb the Appalachians, delightful as that may be, for there are some wonderfully rich and interesting bogs, with their northern plants and animals in the lowlands of the Northeast.

Where northern conifers are still abundant—south of the boreal forests of Canada, northern New England, and the Adirondacks—they usually exist in two different kinds of areas. One is on well-drained uplands, and on the summits of numerous peaks in the southern Appalachians. There, at altitudes above 2,500 feet, grow red spruce, *Picea rubens*, a hardy species gradually driven south by the glaciers, and one of many northern plants on these exposed mountain summits that persists because of a

Searching for dwarf mistletoe and insectivorous plants in a bog

favorable climate. Many of these plants in the southern Appalachians exist today as isolated stands on the highest mountain elevations.

The second area containing boreal plants occurs farther north, in the middle Appalachians and in glaciated regions such as in western New York State, the Pocono Mountains of Pennsylvania, and the Kittatinny Mountains of New Jersey. There one can reach the remnants of the boreal forests by a gentle *descent* from the surrounding hills. Here the hardwood forests look down upon those conifers of the northern muskegs — black spruce, *Picea mariana*, and tamarack, *Larix laricina*.

What geologic events preceded, and were in large measure responsible for the formation of these spruce swamps of the middle Appalachians? How far back from the lifeless conditions of the Pleistocene ice ages have the swamps come on the road of botanical succession? How many northern birds are found breeding in them? What will be the eventual fate of these relict coniferous stands? A brief glimpse at the geologic record will answer the first question; a visit to one of the swamps will answer the next two; and only time will answer the last question.

South of the northern Appalachians of New England, mountain ridges and intervening depressions were formed during a geological thrust from the southeast in the late Paleozoic Era. The uplift of the Appalachians produced conditions unfavorable to the ancient plants of the region, and many species of club mosses, scouring rushes, and seed ferns became extinct. By Jurrassic time, conifers were dominant, but they were overtaken in the subsequent Cretaceous Period by deciduous species of flowering plants which continue to dominate today in most temperate regions of the world (*See Geologic time*).

Late in the Cenozoic Era (about one million years ago) Pleistocene ice masses moved slowly southward from the Arctic,

Purple-fringed orchis

obliterating the plants of the regions they covered and driving animals before them. These ice sheets covered most of the middle Appalachians of southern New York, northern New Jersey, and Pennsylvania. Their bulldozer action piled up much of the earth's mantle so that drainage from valley streams and depressions was impaired. As the earth's temperatures rose once more, the glaciers began to melt and these waters released coarse till, which further complicated drainage by damming streams and creating glacial lakes in the mountain depressions. Eventual invasion of these lakes by plants produced bogs and swamps.

With the northward retreat of the last glacier, lichens advanced upon the exposed land which at this stage resembled an arctic tundra. Sphagnum slowly filled the ponds and lakes and converted them into quaking bogs (the muskegs of the Indian). Sedges and shrubby heaths invaded the moss, and when they were established, spruces, firs, and tamaracks followed. The relict boreal swamps of the middle Appalachians today represent this stage of plant succession. The hardwood forest, a still later stage, has, on the richer, more elevated soil surrounding the mountain swamps, succeeded in establishing itself as the climatic dominant.

The Poconos and Kittatinnies abound with tiny swamps, many of them difficult of access to a stranger who is not guided by a person familiar with the area.

A compass, topographic map, and cloth trail markers are recommended equipment for this and similar exploratory field trips made in unfamiliar territory.

One such swamp readily reached by good roads, lies a few miles northwest of Stroudsburg, Monroe County, Pennsylvania. Designated as Cranberry Swamp on United States Army Engineers' Map, "Pocono Quadrangle," it is frequently referred to, by botanists and local residents alike, as Tannersville Bog.

Cranberry Swamp, or Tannersville Bog, can be reached via Route U.S. 611 by bearing east in Lower Tannersville at a sign marking the location of Tannersville Inn. The visitor travels the one and one half miles from Route 611 to the swamp through pleasant, alternating woodland patches and farmlands. From plowed fields come the penetrating alarm notes of nest-guarding killdeer; from the hedgerows, the measured songs of field sparrows and the bouncing lilt of indigo buntings; from the tops of sugar maples, the caroling of orioles. Here, at approximately 1,000 feet above sea level, no typically boreal species of birds is found.

Where the tall trees begin to thin, the visitor finds himself in the muskeg, that unsteady morass of moss and sedge, clad in a subarctic forest of delicate tamaracks and aromatic spruces. Highbush blueberry, *Vaccinium corymbosum*, makes the undergrowth dense, and the open areas disappear as sheep laurel, *Kalmia angustifolia*, bog laurel, *K. polifolia*, bog rosemary, *Andromeda glaucophylla*, and cassandra, *Chamaedaphne calyculata*, contend with each other for domination and survival.

Where the ground seems unsteady, the visitor would do well to trust his weight to the cassandra shrubs that border the indistinct and sometimes crisscrossing trails. In their proper season, wildflowers blooming here are snake mouth, *Pogonia ophioglossoides*, dragon orchid, *Arethusa bulbosa*, and grass pink, *Calopogon pulchellus*; also purple-fringed orchis, *Habenaria psycodes*, club-spur orchis, *H. clavellata*, and mountain yellow-eyed grass, *Xyris montana*. The white plumes of cotton grass, or hare's-tail, *Eriophorum spissum*, tower over shrubby heaths and the trailing cranberries *Vaccinium oxycoccus* and *V. macrocarpon*.

As one emerges upon the muskeg the two-parted song of the Nashville warbler, beginning in measured tempo, and quickening at the close, comes from the graceful tamaracks, although the songster is sometimes located with difficulty. In some years the rich warbling of purple finches and the easily overlooked call notes of cedar waxwings are added to the insistent song of the Nashville, and the territorial proclamations of the yellow warbler, golden-winged, and chestnut-sided.

At dusk the white-tailed deer become active, and, as shadows lengthen, raccoons, cottontails, opossums, and red foxes are abroad. The beaver and muskrat are still here, and the local people estimate four to five black bears regularly wander through the swamp as part of their "self-appointed rounds."

Though much smaller in extent than the true muskegs of the North, these relict bogs and swamps furnish the students of nearby schools and colleges with an opportunity to study the life forms found in these persistent boreal forests. Graduate students from Rutgers University and the University of Pennsylvania, undergraduates from Union Junior college, 75 miles distant, in Cranford,

Tannersville bog, Pennsylvania

New Jersey, and young naturalists from local high schools visit Cranberry Swamp to study its plants and animals.

What will be the fate of the black spruce tamarack bogs? If untouched by man they should persist for a long time. They will in all probability eventually succumb to natural invasion by red maple, yellow birch, and hemlock, to be followed by numerous species of deciduous trees. Ecologists in those future decades will have to travel far to the north to witness what is, today, near at hand.

Enjoyable as the study of such a bog and boreal swamp may be, there is a practical value they afford that has greater import to the local residents than a listing of its plants and wildlife. The devastating floods that swept through Monroe County, Pennsylvania, in the wake of hurricane Diane in 1955 clearly demonstrated their value in flood control. The water-holding capacity of this relatively untouched swamp, with its stream banks clothed by plants, prevented torrents from washing out the downstream bridges. Any swamp or bog with an abundance of water-loving sphagnum moss, and its accompanying sedges, shrubs, and trees, could have performed service equal to that of the Cranberry. Nearby rivulets and creeks with eroded banks and with no swamps along their courses were swelled to sizable rivers. The torrential force of the floodwaters dislodged bridges, destroyed homes, and took a heavy toll of human life. Surveying the damage in the county later, and realizing the value of such wa-

These emergent aquatic plants are rushes

ter-holding land as Cranberry Swamp, a committee of local residents undertook to preserve it.

In January 1957, Tannersville Bog Preserve was bought for $2,000 with the help of many local groups, including P.T.A., Boy Scouts, and civic organizations. In the future, the groups hope to increase the size of the preserve which is to be maintained in a wild state, the title to be held in the name of the Nature Conservancy.

In the future decades, as the sun moves in an arc across the sky, one hopes it will still brighten unspoiled sand dunes, salt marshes, pine barrens, deciduous forests, prairies, plains, mountain lakes, deserts, and redwood forests. There, young naturalists may still enjoy seeing the wildlife of natural areas. The present generation owes it to those that follow to preserve as many unspoiled habitats as is possible. It cannot afford not to.
—D.F. and S.F.

BOG (*See also Muskeg*)

BONEFISH
Other Common Names—Silver king
Scientific Name—*Albula vulpes*
Family—Albulidae (bonefishes)
Order—Semionotiformes
Size—May grow to more than 3½ feet long and 13 pounds in weight
Range—Found in all tropical seas and, rarely, as far north as Cape Cod. Sometimes reported in the Chesapeake and Middle Atlantic regions

The bonefish is the only representative of its family. Its body lines are smooth and streamlined; its piglike snout extends beyond its lower jaw. Both jaws are lined with strong, rounded teeth, and its eyes are nearly covered with a thick transparent membrane.

The bonefish has one dorsal fin with 15 well-developed rays. The fin is situated in the center of the back. The anal fin is much smaller, having only eight rays, but is also well developed. It is positioned to the rear of the underside of the fish.

Bonefishes are a brilliant silver, with a tint of olive-brown on the back and sides. They are sometimes confused with the ladyfish, or big-eyed herring, *Elops saurus*. Most fishermen can tell one from the other by looking for the characteristic head and nose shape of the bonefish. Also, in contrast to the bonefish, the big-eyed herring has 20 rays in its dorsal fin and 13 in its anal fin. In addition, bonefishes have observably larger scales.

The bonefish eats mollusks and other shelled sea animals. It uses its snoutlike nose to dig up these creatures and then breaks their shells by pressing them against its rounded teeth. For its size, the bonefish is an extremely hard fighter when hooked, and fishermen consider it an outstanding game fish.

Young bonefishes are very different from adults. They are more elongated and have smaller heads. Also, they are transparent, making them nearly invisible in the water. As they mature they "shrink" three inches in length. —M.R.

BONITO
Atlantic Bonito
Other Common Names—Common bonito, skipjack, horse mackerel
Scientific Name—*Sarda sarda*
Family—Scombridae (mackerels and tuna)
Order—Perciformes
Size—Up to about 3 feet long and 12 pounds in weight
Range—In warm marine waters on both the North American and European sides of the Atlantic and in the Mediterranean.

Bonito

Has been reported as far north as the waters of Nova Scotia and Scandinavia.

The Atlantic bonito's body is thick and stout (about ¼ as deep as it is long). It tapers frontward to a pointed nose and rearward to a slender tailfin base. The fish has two dorsal fins. The front one, beginning close to the head, has 21 spines and is about one-third the length of the fish's body. The top margin of the fin is almost a straight line and descends gradually as it continues along the back. The rear dorsal fin is small and elongated. Its margin is deeply concave. The rear dorsal fin is followed by seven or eight small dorsal finlets. The anal fin is shaped like the rear dorsal fin and is followed by seven small anal finlets. The fish's mouth is relatively large and gapes back to the rear margin of the eyes.

The Atlantic bonito has a blue-black back. Its upper sides are lighter and have 7 to 20 parallel, dark blue bands running obliquely from the edge of the back toward the rear gill openings. Its lower sides and belly are silvery. When young, the fish has 10 to 12 dark blue vertical bars on each side.

The Atlantic bonito travels offshore in large schools. It feeds ravenously on small fishes and squid and can often be seen leaping from the water as it pursues its prey. It is a good food fish but is not commonly eaten in the United States or Canada. It is similar to its relative, the tuna, and is often canned in the same manner. When this is done, however, the label must be marked "bonito."

Other species of bonito include the Pacific bonito, *Sarda chiliensis*, and the striped bonito, *Sarda orientalis*. *Sarda chiliensis*, commonly known as the California bonito, is larger and heavier than the Atlantic bonito. —M.R.

BOTANY

Botany is the scientific study of plants. Apart from the usual subdivision into specialized disciplines (*see* Biology) which is characteristic of laboratory courses, botany as a field of outdoor exploration is conveniently divided into two specialties: (1) *floristics,* the study of individual plants — whether trees, wild flowers, grasses, etc. — and (2) *vegetation,* the study of communities of plants.

Because of the importance of plants to man, as food and fiber, a large group of special botanical studies are grouped separately as Economic Botany.
—R.C.C.

BOTULISM

Avian botulism, or food poisoning, also known as "western duck sickness," is a duck disease caused by eating foods infected with the bacterium *Clostridium botulinum.* It occurs only during a brief period in late summer or early fall. During those few weeks, however, the loss of birdlife from this malady is sometimes appalling. In 1932 more than 250,000 ducks died on the north shore flats of Great Salt Lake. In 1955, even after extensive preventive measures had been taken, more than 19,000 dead and dying birds were picked up in the same area.

This disease of migrating waterfowl shocked western naturalists as early as 1900. It has also been reported from Canada, Australia, South America, and other parts of the world, always with the same natural conditions prevailing when it occurred.

Early suppositions, stemming from the fact that the disease usually broke out in areas in which the soil was highly alkaline, held that the sickness was simply poisoning caused by ingesting these inorganic substances.

In 1914 the United States Bureau of Biological Survey (now the Fish and Wildlife Service) assigned Alexander Wetmore to the task of studying the disease. Working mainly in the Bear River, Utah, area and other western alkaline lakes, Wetmore made many valuable observations during 1914, 1915, and 1916.

Migrating ducks (above) are often infected with avian botulism, or western duck sickness, that kills them by the hundreds of thousands (below)

Picking up sick and dead ducks at the Bear River Migratory Bird Refuge

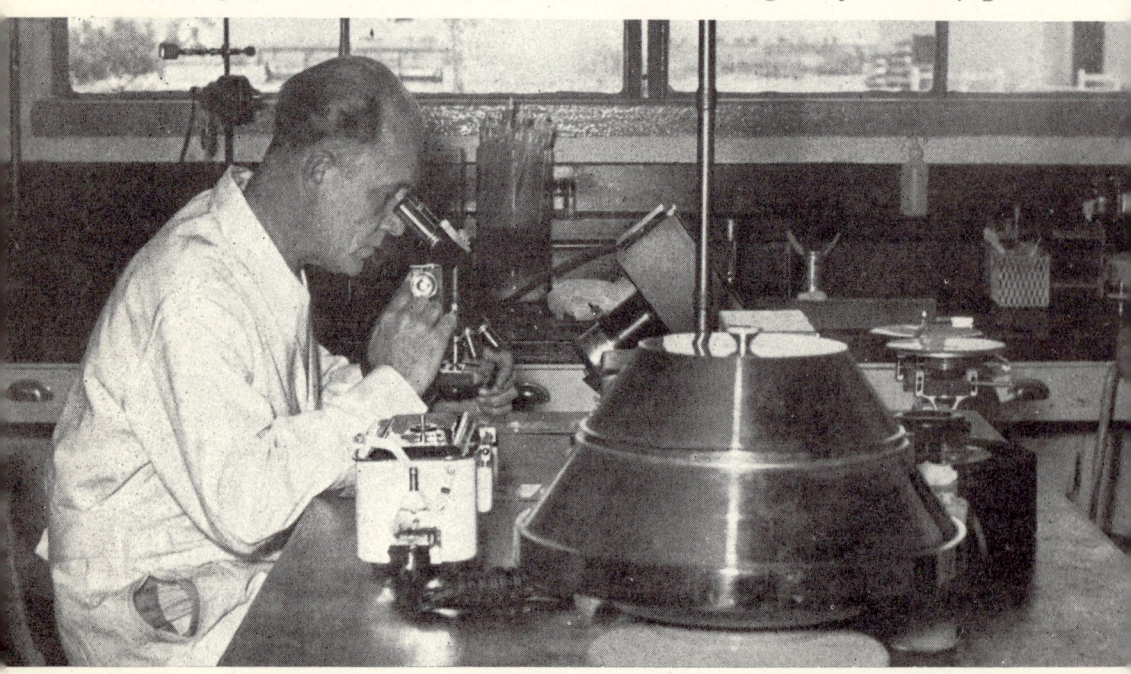

Studying mud and invertebrates taken from the waters of the Bear River Refuge where thousands of waterfowl feed

His conclusions, however, were much the same as previous theories—that the death of so many birds was caused principally by the soluble alkali in the water—specifically, the chlorides of magnesium and calcium.

Later investigators, however, noted that these conclusions appeared to conflict with conditions observed elsewhere in which ducks remained healthy while feeding on lakes of very high alkalinity, yet sometimes sickened and died when feeding in waters that had weaker concentrations of inorganic salts.

In 1924 Ida A. Bengston, working in the laboratories of the United States Public Health Service, isolated and first described the bacterium, *Clostridium botulinum*, Type C. Later investigations have repeatedly shown the toxin of *Clostridium botulinum* (also sometimes called *Bacillus botulinus*) to be present in the bloodstream of infected ducks captured during these summer epizootics, or epidemic outbreaks of the disease.

Diagnosing the cause was one thing, preventing it was quite another. Although the alkaline shores of reflooded lakes might be pinpointed as the prime sources of trouble, there was no way of treating such areas. Indeed, because the western water table has dropped over the years, and drainage has been disrupted or has disappeared altogether, the number of

Sick birds are given injections of antitoxin at regular intervals in the hospital; a high percentage of the treated birds recover

BOTULISM

danger areas has increased.

Also, as human population pressure has restricted migratory waterfowl to fewer and fewer nesting areas and flyway routes, the concentration of migratory waterfowl in these danger areas has grown.

The staff at Bear River National Wildlife Refuge, in Utah, is often overwhelmed with work during outbreaks of botulism. Workers and student volunteers pick up ducks that are dead or seriously affected. The living ducks are cleansed and given clean food and water. Many recover quickly with this simple treatment.

Clostridium botulinum occurs almost everywhere, so it cannot be localized and destroyed. It exists on decaying matter of almost any type, often anaerobically, that is without free oxygen, and it forms many spores.

These spores are almost indestructible. They are capable of surviving hours of boiling in water, and years of drought and freezing. To fight the disease chemically would be prohibitively expensive and of doubtful value. The only immediate answer is to prevent the concentration of the bacterium in vital areas where its toxin in dangerous amounts would be available to waterfowl—even

Inspecting a group of convalescing ducks under treatment at the Refuge

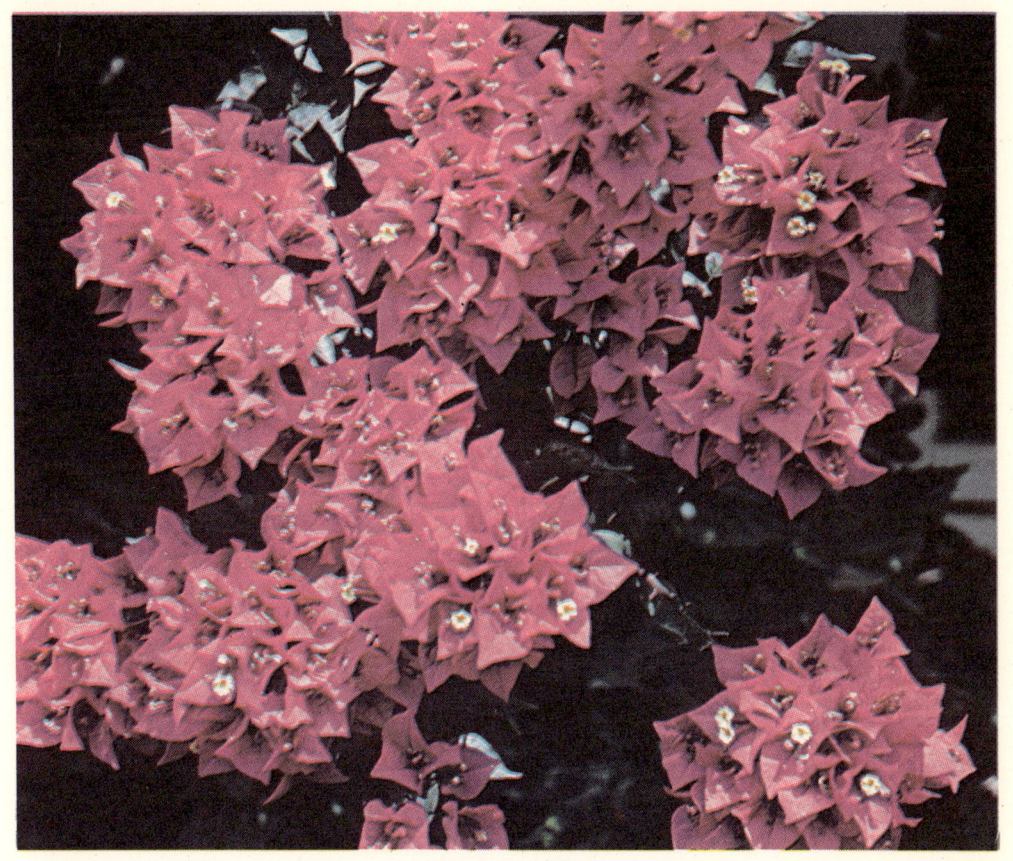

Bougainvillea

if this meant driving away the birds. This can be done by deepening the water over the danger areas during the migratory seasons. The birds are then forced to feed farther from the mud which apparently contains the greatest concentrations of toxin. —F.A.T.

BOUGAINVILLEA
Other Common Names—None
Scientific Name—*Bougainvillea glabra*
Family—Nyctaginaceae (four o'clock family)
Range—Native to tropical South America
Habitat—Tropical regions; often twines around other plants
Time of Blooming—Continuous

The bougainvillea belongs to the four o'clock family — *Nyctaginaceae* — which consists of about 300 species of herbs, shrubs, and trees. These species are widely distributed in subtropical to tropical regions and confined, for the most part, to the New World.

The bougainvillea itself has about 13 species, all native to South America. Because of their large colorful flowers some of these are cultivated as ornamental porch and arbor vines in southern regions of the United States. Small plantings are sometimes grown in pots in more temperate regions of the north and entire vines are grown in hothouses.

The flowers range from purple and magenta to delicate shades of pink and salmon and to cream and white.

The plant gets its name from the French navigator Louis Antoine de Bougainville. —G.A.B.

BOUNTY SYSTEM

Bounties have been paid for the destruction of wild animals for thousands of years. Bounties were among man's earliest attempts to change his environment or to limit species of wild animals he considered undesirable.

Ancient writings indicate that bounties in wolves were paid by the Greeks nearly 3,000 years ago. For centuries, bounties have been offered throughout most of Europe. In North America, New Hampshire passed its first bounty law in 1679, and there is evidence of bounties being paid by the colonies earlier than that. Almost all the states, provinces, and territories in North America have employed the system.

The original purpose of paying bounties was the protection of domestic animals and crops. The system later was employed in hopes of reducing game losses that resulted from predatory animals. In the past 30 years, however, biologists have formed new opinions about the value of predatory species. Many animals that were for centuries labeled "bad" have been found to have economic values ranging from neutral to highly beneficial. Consequently, the bounty system is now being reexamined.

Not only have bounties proved to be biologically untenable but, from the economic viewpoint, a financial fiasco. Millions of dollars have been paid out in bounties. Taxes, game and fish department funds, hunting and fishing license receipts, and dog license fees are only a few of the sources used to finance the system. The tremendous cost and labor involved in maintaining the bounty system could readily be used for more constructive projects. For example, the acquisition and improvement of wildlife habitats is a major goal in wildlife conservation projects at the present time, but these activities are seriously hampered by lack of funds. Yet several million dollars each year are wasted on useless bounties.

In 1960, by conservative estimate, over $2,000,000 was spent for bounties and administration of the bounty system within the United States. South Dakota alone spent $192,000 on bounties, or nearly 40 percent of its $523,000 game and fish allocation. An additional $90,000 was spent for predator and rodent control programs, tying up more than half of the department's total funds in animal control measures.

Some states have shifted the payment of bounties from their game and fish departments to local counties or townships. This does not relieve the taxpayer; in some instances it increases the possibility of fraud and misrepresentation. Nevertheless, this shift might be considered an improvement, since it allows the game and fish departments to make better use of funds previously spent for bounty payments and for administration of the system.

Although evidence against the validity of the bounty system is overwhelming, the idea still remains deeply embedded in wildlife laws. In 1963, 33 states paid bounties as compared to 27 states that paid bounties in 1950. The animals listed as predators as well as the number of states offering bounties changes from year to year. During 1960, bounties were offered on 33 varieties of birds, and reptiles in the United States and Canada. The fox, coyote, and bobcat headed the list in the number of claims and total monies paid.

State wildlife biologists generally have little authority over bounties. Their main contribution is in the form of advice. Unfortunately, it is not often given the respect it deserves. Game and fish departments have made reports to guide their state legislatures in the use of bounties, but in many instances the reports have been ignored or misinterpreted.

The reluctance to eliminate bounties is due to several factors. One is the lack of understanding of the facts of

BOUNTY SYSTEM 309

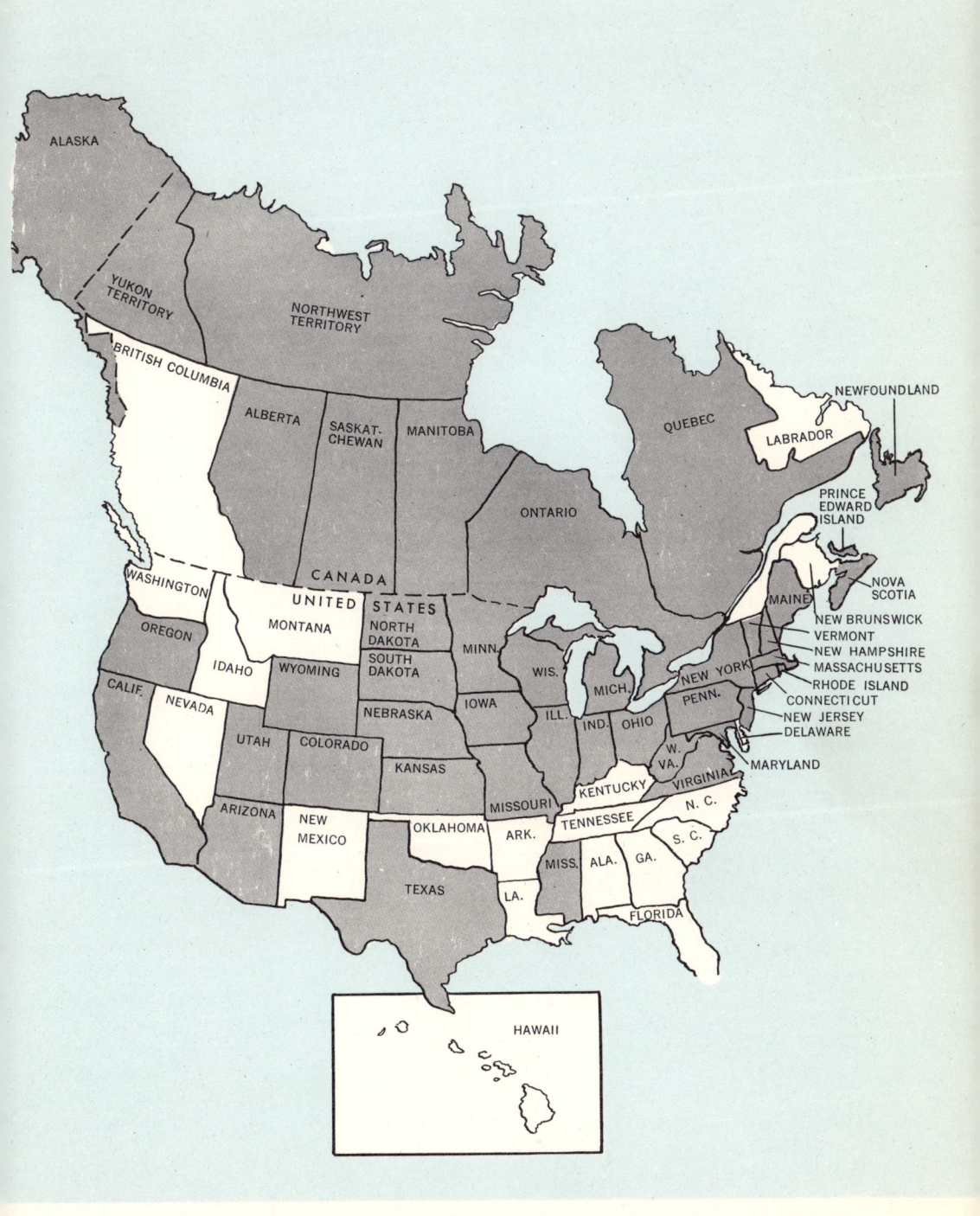

Shaded area shows 33 states and 10 Canadian provinces in which wildlife bounty laws are in effect. No information available on New Brunswick. (Hawaii inset is not in scale)

Red squirrel

Coyote

Long-tailed weasel

ecology or a refusal to accept them. In some minds the fact that bounties have existed for years is sufficient ground to continue giving them. A more basic reason, however, is the monetary return. Bounties provide additional income for hundreds of people; a few hunters and trappers may make the greater part of their living from them. Consequently, bounties are often subjected to political pressures. Local politicians sometimes support the bounty system as part of their election platforms — which amounts to destroying wildlife for unsound reasons in order to obtain votes.

The chief supports of bounties, however, are the outdated ideas and false conceptions that have existed for generations. Many early books on natural history contained a great deal of misinformation about the habits of wild animals. Possibly even more errors have passed down from one generation to another as hearsay and folklore. In colonial America the exaggerated ferocity of wild animals was as mistaken a belief as the belief in witches. Unfortunately, many of these legendary beliefs still persist.

During the 300 years that bounties have been paid in North America, the larger predators — principally the wolf, coyote, fox, mountain lion, and bobcat — have been the primary victims. The timber wolf, the first animal for which bounties were paid in North America, retreated to the wilderness as civilization advanced and its natural food supply decreased. As cattle were introduced into new and uncultivated areas, the wolf bounties increased, since wolves were considered a dangerous menace to livestock. In one locality a single wolf was credited with destroying over $25,000 worth of cattle and range animals. Bounties ran as high as $150 per wolf. Congress also appropriated large sums to eliminate the timber wolf and other livestock predators. As a result, the baying of the timber wolf, a vocal symbol of the American wilderness, is rarely heard in the United States today. The wolf's present range is limited mainly to Canada and Alaska.

Biologists are generally agreed that the destruction of the timber wolf's natural range and intense predator control programs were the chief factors responsible for its decline. Bounties, although not as important as the other two factors mentioned, certainly helped accelerate the decline of the wolf population. Sixteen states, provinces and territories still pay wolf bounties, which range as high as $50 per animal. The decreasing number of bounty claims in the United States indicates how the wolf population is declining. Possibly many of these "wolf" claims were actually wolflike dogs or coyotes.

In Ontario, where most of the wolf bounties are paid today, biologists have accumulated some interesting facts regarding the ecology of the wolf. Bounties were inaugurated in 1905 in hopes that they would increase the Ontario deer population, but they have had little or no effect upon either the wolf or deer population. Substantial wolf and deer populations are found living side by side. In fact, the largest number of bounty claims originated in areas where the deer are thriving best. Biologists concluded that the spread of civilization which resulted in a decrease in the amount of available cover for the deer—and not predation—were the main factors responsible for decrease in the size of the deer herds.

Studies of other predatory mammals have shown that bounties may kill off surplus members of a species, leaving a strong breeding stock that keeps the population at a high level.

Studies of red and gray fox populations show, for example, that bounties have little effect upon the natural ups and downs in fox populations. Foxes, like many other animals in the northern

Mountain lion

Bobcat

Northern pocket gopher

312 BOUNTY SYSTEM

Raccoon

Woodchuck

Eastern mole

United States, tend to be cyclic in their numbers and these natural fluctuations cannot be correlated with the payment of bounties.

The fox has been accused, among other things, of a major role in the decrease of gamebirds. In Michigan, foxes were blamed for the decrease in the numbers of pheasant during the latter part of the 1940's. Nevertheless, biologists discovered on Pelee Island, Ontario, about 60 miles southeast of Detroit on Lake Erie, that the island's pheasant population fell at the same time as that in nearby Michigan, even though foxes were absent. Other studies have shown rising pheasant and fox populations existing side by side. Foxes do eat pheasants but it is very doubtful that they have much influence on the population of pheasant, or of any other gamebird.

That some foxes eat chickens has also been used to rationalize the payment of fox bounties, but, again, a closer look at the ecology of the fox reveals a conflicting picture. While a few foxes have a fancy for raiding the chicken house, studies of their food habits reveal that only a very small percentage of the fox's diet consists of poultry. In fact, most foxes do not eat chickens at all. It is unjustifiable to declare all-out war upon a species when the economic damage caused by a small minority is limited—and even more so when the majority of the species is beneficial.

An estimated $1,000,000 was spent on fox bounties in the United States and Canada during 1960, which was nearly half of all bounties paid for that year. Michigan alone spent over $500,-000 during a four-year period. The fox's popularity as number one on the bounty lists has not diminished since then. Now bounties in 22 states and provinces (a distinction shared only by the bobcat) for foxes lead all other animals in numbers killed and bounty dollars paid. Judging from the amount of money paid for fox bounties, it would probably be less expensive to subsidize farmers for their losses.

There are, however, better and more economical solutions to losses by predators. The best solution involves preventive measures and the killing of only those predators that are causing damage, rather than exterminating an entire species. Proper enclosures that would prevent depredation by predators are another solution. The cost would be far less than the time and effort spent in pursuing the predator.

Where enclosures or preventive measures are not feasible a solution adopted in 1945 by the Missouri Conservation Commission has proven effective. The commission had found the bounty system impractical and had adopted an extensive predator control program. A trapper-instructor was employed to help farmers who requested aid in stopping losses caused by predators. The farmer received instructions on how to trap the predator causing the damage. He was also told of beneficial predation among wild animals as distinguished from losses of domestic animals. Precautions that could be taken were also suggested to him that would reduce the danger to beneficial animals, both wild and domestic.

The Missouri commission found that farmers ceased trapping operations as soon as the offending predators were caught. This program was inexpensive to operate and a definite success. Four other states have since adopted similar programs.

The majority of bounties for coyotes are paid in the midwestern states, although poisons and other control methods are also employed, principally in the western states. Probably no other predator in North America is so severely persecuted and at the same time so grossly misunderstood as the coyote. In an intensive study of the food habits of coyotes in agricultural areas of Kansas, biologists discovered their good

Porcupine

Badger

Black-tailed jackrabbit

habits are as follows: Coyotes eat the flesh of those animals most readily available to them. Wild birds and mammals are taken on the basis of availability and need, and game birds suffer no serious predation. Sheep, pigs, and calves are killed occasionally, but most of the livestock eaten is in the form of carrion. Coyotes sometimes learn to kill poultry and other farm animals when dead livestock is discarded.

Furthermore, a high percentage of the coyote's diet consists of rabbits and rodents that compete with domestic stock for grazing crops. In recognition of this, in South Dakota, California, Colorado, and a few other Western states, ranchers have begun posting their ranges against coyote hunting.

Coyote hunters employ methods ranging from the use of inexpensive steel traps to low-flying aircraft. Bounties in some states are as high as $30 for each coyote although the average is about $12. In 1960 an estimated $900,000 was paid out by 18 states and provinces that offered bounties for coyotes. This figure is dwarfed by the amounts paid for predator control programs against the coyote sponsored by federal, state, and local agencies.

In six western states some of the highest bounties are paid for the mountain lion, or cougar. In California it is possible to collect both a state and a county bounty, or a total of $135, for a single mountain lion. The state of California has paid bounties on over 12,500 mountain lions since 1907, and individual counties have paid additional thousands. Yet mountain lions, like wolves, are no longer serious predators of livestock. The small number of mountain lions remaining deserves to be preserved for future generations.

The bobcat is another animal that is on almost every bounty list, largely because it preys on deer. In many states where the bounty on bobcats is high, the deer population has increased beyond the carrying capacity of the land, and a reduction of the deer herd has become desirable. In many other states the bounties on bobcats continue even though bobcats have become scarce.

Small animals, predatory and nonpredatory alike, have been on the bounty lists for decades. Some of these bounties have totaled unusually large amounts. In one 20-year period before weasels were removed from Pennsylvania's bounty list, the state game commission paid over $1,000,000 in weasel bounties.

South Dakota paid bounties on more than 16,000 badgers in 1960. Some counties in Oregon and Iowa have recently begun to pay bounties on moles. Alaska is still offering bounties for some species of seals, and many states and counties pay bounties on crows, magpies, blue jays, blackbirds, hawks, owls, ground squirrels, woodchucks, raccoons, and other small animals.

The removal of bounty laws will not be a simple task and even after the goal has been accomplished, constant vigilance will be necessary to prevent reintroduction. In the case of state bounties, a statewide cooperative program among interested conservation-minded organizations would probably be the most effective means. This would involve the usual procedure of writing letters and petitions to state legislators urging the introduction of a bill to remove existing bounty laws.

In some states it might also be wise to request an extension predator control program, which would operate upon request of the parties directly involved in depredations. This, in a sense, would give the proponents of the bounty system even fewer arguments in their favor.

Where bounties are administered on a county or lower level, it may be necessary to work through these levels, providing there are not too many. If a large number of counties pay bounties

While the porcupine is now protected in many states, the coyote continues to be heavily persecuted by bounty hunters, even though it rarely attacks domestic species

it may be much simpler to seek state action.

Educational programs offer an additional approach. Conservation organizations can disseminate facts about the bounty system and help to change the bad image that some animals have, especially in the eyes of young children. Ecology is receiving greater emphasis in formal education than ever before; colleges and high schools are including more ecological principles as an integral part of their biology curricula. There are also indications that basic ecological ideas are finding their way into the elementary levels.

If these trends continue and the effects are stimulating enough, a greater understanding of wildlife, resulting in fewer abuses, may be the result.–H.C.L.

BROMELIAD (*See Epiphyte*)

Bryce Canyon National Park, Utah

BRYCE CANYON NATIONAL PARK
Location—Southern Utah
Size—56 square miles
Mammals—Cougars, coyotes, gray foxes, bobcats, porcupines, mule deer
Birdlife—Roadrunners, red-shafted flickers, many songbirds in summer
Plants—Firs, ponderosa pines, foxtail pines, trembling aspens, junipers, chaparral

The rocks of this national park, formed of pink and white sandstones and limestones that have been eroded into fantastic shapes by the work of wind and moisture, make it a scenic wonder. Roads run to the rim of the canyon, and horseback trails run through the park. Lectures on the geology and forms of life existing in the park are given every evening at the lodge and around the campfire from May 10 to November 1.
Accommodations—Campground, cabins, rooms; horses and guides are available
Headquarters—Springdale, Utah

—G.B.S.

BRYOPHYTE

Liverworts, hornworts, and mosses belong to the second major division of the plant kingdom, that of the bryophytes. They are closely related to the algae in development but are more advanced in their adaptations for living on the land.

None of the plants in this subkingdom have the woody tissues that the higher plants use to lift their chlorophyll-bearing tissues into the sunlight. They also lack true roots and leaves, although some of them have structures that resemble these specialized organs.

Bryophytes usually live in damp, shady areas where they ordinarily grow in dense mats. A few kinds live in deserts; they are able to suspend most of their activities until moisture comes to them. Others live under arctic conditions. Their ideal habitat, however, is a bog, and there they can compete successfully with most of the higher plants (See *Bog*).

—G.B.S.

BUCKEYE
Ohio Buckeye
Other Common Names—Fetid buckeye, stinking buckeye
Scientific Name—*Aesculus glabra*
Family—Hippocastanaceae (buckeye family)
Range—Western Pennsylvania to eastern Nebraska, south to Oklahoma and upland North Carolina. State tree of Ohio
Habitat—Differs from horse chestnut, *Aesculus hippocastanum,* mainly in its smaller, more delicate leaves and more slender, less shiny winter buds. Usually a tree of rich lowland soils
Leaves—Compound, usually with five leaflets, finely toothed; up to eight inches across; usually yellowish in late summer
Bark—Much as in horse chestnut
Flowers—Smaller, more slender clusters than horse chestnut, and of a yellowish-green color. These appear a bit earlier in spring and have a strong odor

Horse chestnut (left); Ohio buckeye (right)

Fruit—The burs are smaller than the horse chestnut's with a few short prickles. The nut has a small "eye" area and is also poisonous

Five trees native to North America, and one that has been introduced from Europe, are in the Hippocastanaceae—the buckeye family. The distinguishing characteristics of this group are the large, palmate leaves, usually with five to seven leaflets; the leathery and shiny coat of the large chestnutlike seed with its large pale scar on one side; and the bell—or tube-shaped flowers that grow in a pyramidal mass called a panicle.

The red buckeye, growing from Florida to Virginia, has red flowers. The bottle-brush buckeye, a white-flowered shrub, grows from South Carolina to Florida. The yellow, or sweet, buckeye is a tree with yellow flowers, and is native to Pennsylvania, Illinois, Georgia, and the area between those states. The California buckeye has flowers that range from white to rose. (*See also Horse Chestnut*)

—G.B.S.

BUFFALO (*See Bison*)

BUG

Only the insects of the order Hemiptera have a clear title to the name of bug, though many people apply the term to any insect. The order contains about 50,000 species. One of the few features they have in common, although they are not the only insect order with this feature, is the piercing and sucking mouthparts. While most bugs use this equipment for feeding on plants, some species inject a quick-acting poison into the tissues of other insects, and then suck out the soft interior.

The order Hemiptera has two great divisions based on the structure of the wings. The suborder Heteroptera has the inner part of their two front wings thickened and shell-like, while the outer part is membranous, as is all of the second pair of wings. In the other suborder, the Homoptera, both sets of wings are alike. This simple division is complicated by the fact that several families of bugs have lost their wings entirely.

A few families of true bugs include the shield bugs, stink bugs, cinch bugs, ambush bugs, assassin bugs, bedbugs,

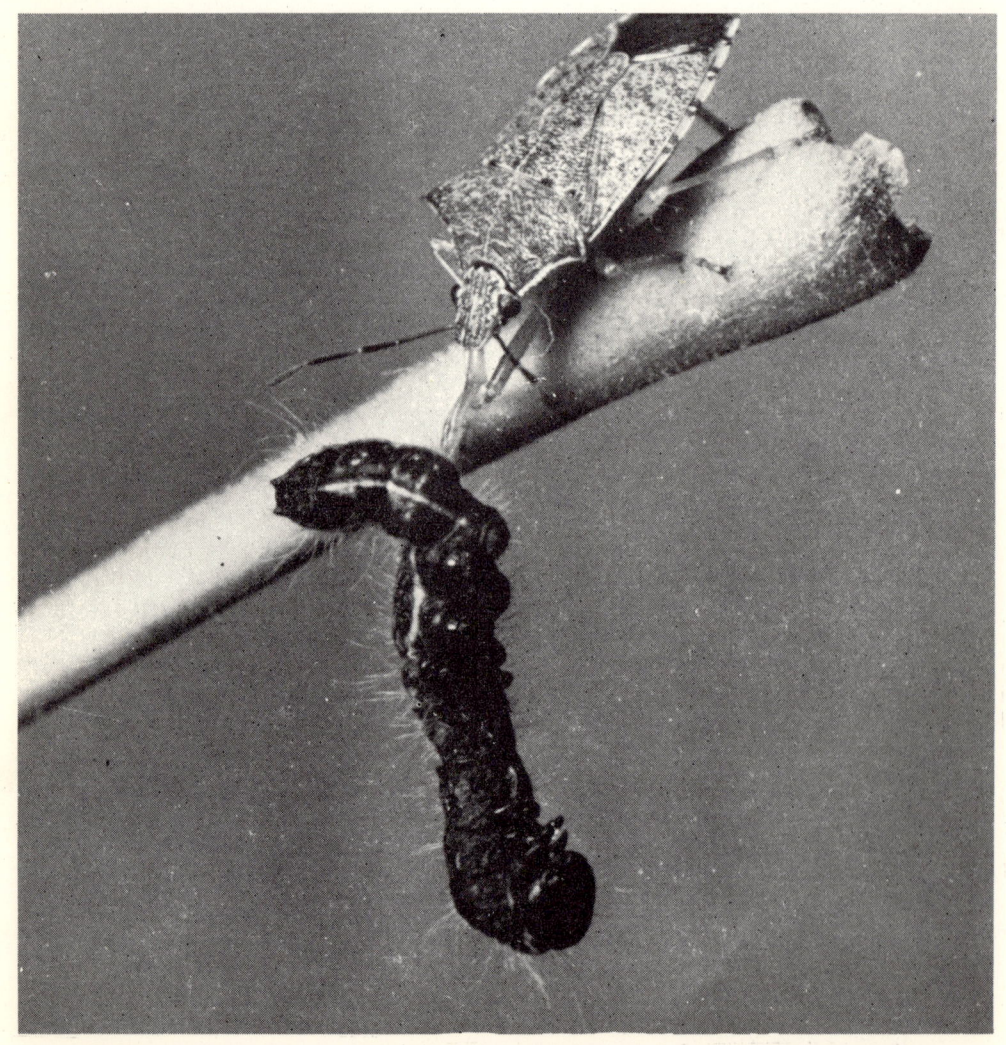

A spined soldier bug sucks the body juices from a paralyzed caterpillar

The last-stage nymph of the spined soldier bug was thrashed about in the air and slammed to the ground several times by the hairy caterpillar, larva of walnut moth, before the bug's poison paralyzed its larger prey

water striders, water scorpions, cicadas, spittlebugs, leafhoppers, aphids, mealybugs, and scale insects. Many of the bugs are parasites upon birds and mammals. (*See Parasite: Some Insect Parasites of Birds*). Some kinds not only rob the host of blood, but inject it with harmful bacteria and viruses. Other kinds, such as the aphids and scale insects, are among the worst of the plant parasites. (*See also Mexican Chicken Bug under Parasite*) —G.B.S.

Bordered Soldier Bug
Other Common Names—Anchorage bug, stinkbug
Scientific Name—*Stiretrus ancharago*
Family—Pentatomidae (stinkbugs)
Order—Hemiptera
Size—Length, one-half inch
Range—Across central and northern United States

Spined Soldier Bug
Other Common Names—Stinkbug
Scientific Name—*Podisus maculiventris*
Family—Pentatomidae (stinkbugs)
Order—Hemiptera
Size—Length, one-half inch
Range—Across central and northern United States

When one considers the army of insects classified under the family name of Pentatomidae—better known as stinkbugs—the wonder is that there is room on the globe for them, much less for other insect families. Over 4,000 species of pentatomids have been identified and named and 300 of them live within the borders of the United States.

In the main, these bugs drink plant juices, but there are some that vary their diet to include the body fluids of fellow insects. Still others thrive on insect fare alone.

Two of these predatory species are the spined solider bug, *Podisus maculiventris*, and the bordered soldier bug, *Stiretrus ancharago*, both of which consume their insect contemporaries. Unattractive or not, their voracious appetites serve a useful purpose in helping nature keep its biological balance, not to mention the destruction of many cutworms and potato beetle larvae (*See Balance of Nature, and under Biological Control*).

In appearance the spined soldier bug tribe can scarcely be distinguished from its plant-sipping relatives except for an opaque brown streak at the transparent tip of the wing cases. The spined soldier bug is ochre-brown in color, with sharply spined shoulders, and is about the diameter of a man's little fingernail. The bordered soldier bug is the same size but goes all out for gay colors and variety in markings. No two bugs are marked exactly alike. They are usually a shade of red or orange (or sometimes a grayish-tan) marked with black. The males are smaller than their mates and are usually brighter in color.

There is a difference, also, in the mating habits of soldier bugs. To the spined species, the act seems a necessary nuisance. On occasion pairs will mate while the female is feeding. With the bordered bugs, however, especially the gaily decorated males, mating seems a great adventure. The males parade their black wing membranes flashing them to right and left whenever a female comes near.

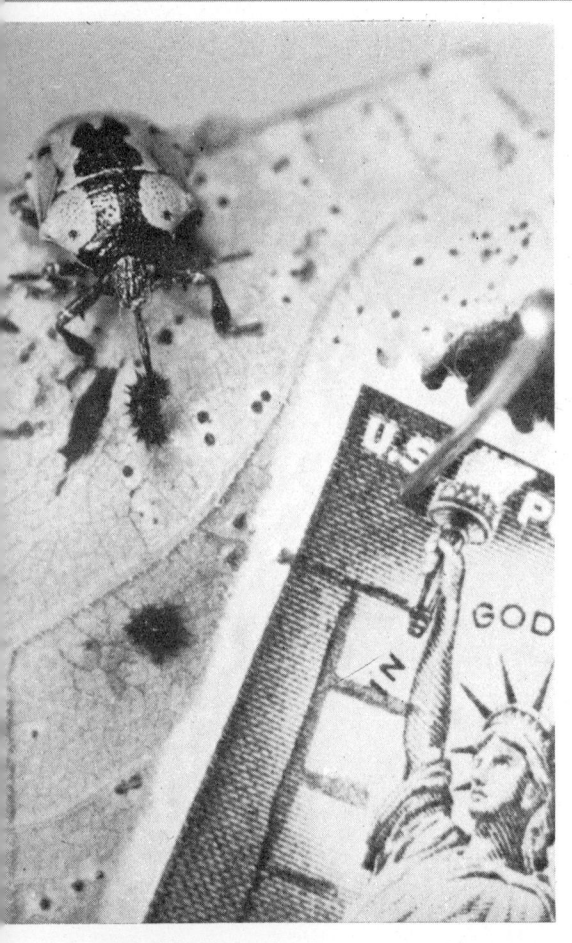

The bordered soldier bug destroys entire colonies of crescent spot butterfly caterpillars. (Stamp shows comparative size)

The young of both of these species, developing from bronze-colored eggs laid in clusters on any available surface, come into the world dressed very much alike. When observed through a hand lens the hatchlings can be seen to be shiny black, except for their rounded abdomens that are dark red.

For a day or two following their hatching, the young hatchlings seem reluctant to leave their birthplace. They cling to the empty shells, sometimes forming small mounds as they cluster together while awaiting their first molt.

Following this, they quickly disperse, seeking tiny soil mites and other minute arthropods (See *Arthropod*), gradually taking larger game as they grow older. At this stage—about their third molt—a decided change in their foraging habits begins. Hatchlings of the spined soldier bug may attack caterpillars many times their own weight and girth.

Bordered soldier bugs, however, usually attack creatures considerably smaller than themselves. They have been observed walking about with the small larvae of moths or cabbage butterflies impaled on their beaks.

Some years ago a bordered soldier bug, between sunset and nine o'clock the following morning, was observed taking 16 quarter-grown procris larvae from their grape-leaf "pasture." Only four of the herd were left and one of these, when found, was on the beak of the bug. One of these bugs was once observed eating its way through a young caterpillar herd, requiring but 10 minutes of feeding on each individual and leaving nothing behind but the shriveled skins of the victims.

As hunters these two species of pentatomids also differ sharply. While the bordered soldier bugs, in taking smaller victims, have little to fear from their victims, they nevertheless shield their snouts with their peculiarly shaped forelegs.

The spined soldier bugs, in their attacks upon such large creatures as full-grown tent caterpillars or the matured larvae of the Gulf fritillary butterfly, approach with care and caution. There is no rushing in as with the bordered soldier bugs. This cautious approach seems quite unnecessary, for the intended victim usually pays no attention to the brown bug creeping about its flanks. Also, when the bug decides to move in for the "kill," it seems the selected moment is no better nor worse than the several that preceded it.

But once the spined soldier bug's harpoon-beak has struck, there is no escape for its prey. The attacker immediately starts a backward movement that continues until the victim (benumbed by a paralyzing agent in the bug's saliva) loses its foothold and, supported by the pentatomidal beak, swings free. The feeding bug then seems to go into a trance, apparently taking no interest in its surroundings or events that are taking place nearby.

Most of the thousands of relatives of these soldier bugs are drinkers of plant sap. It is intriguing to speculate by what evolutionary procedure the soldier bugs became such relentless hunters of other insects. —R.J.D. and M.L.D.

Wheel Bug
Other Common Names — None
Scientific Name — *Arilus cristatus*
Family — Reduviidae (assassin bugs)
Order — Hemiptera
Size — Length, one inch
Range — Lives in the southern United States and from New Mexico and Okalahoma to Pennsylvania and Florida

Some members of the insect kingdom are more or less nondescript, with one insect closely resembling many another, but this is not true of the wheel bug, *Arilus cristatus*. This bug has a striking feature that sets it apart from any other. This is the semicircular, crownlike crest that sets atop the prothorax, an odd "cogwheel."

The wheel bug has a distinctive "cogwheel" crest

The wheel bug is one of the assassins of the family Reduviidae. Its favorite habitat is among flowers, where it awaits the appearance of unwary prey. For the most part, it is a predator only on insects—although at times it attacks warm-blooded animals—and if disturbed, it will stab its sharp beak into man. The attack of the wheel bug is often painful (which also helps set it apart from the mostly innocuous insects) and it is best avoided when possible.

Two large eyes bulge from a long, slim head and help add to its strangely grotesque appearance. Two ocelli are generally behind the eyes, and in front of them is a sharp beak riding in a furrow. Sounds are made by rubbing its beak against its delicate striations.

The legs of the wheel bug are strong, and the forelegs, although not especially adapted for grasping, are surprisingly powerful.

A wheel bug was observed to clutch and hold a grasshopper's long back leg in spite of every attempt the grasshopper made to get away. In a last desperate round of gyrations, the struggling grasshopper tore away, leaving one of its legs in the bug's strong grip while it made its escape on the other five.

Eggs of the wheel bug are laid in clusters on leaves—like other plant bugs in the order Hemiptera. The eggs, standing upright, look like tiny milk bottles grouped in a little round mass. Hatching young ones are often blood-red, with black marks, and closely resemble the adults. These nymphs, too, prey on other insects, which they stab with a beak oozing a poisonous, paralyzing fluid.

The wheel bug is considered highly useful to mankind. It helps to control many leaf-eating caterpillars, and the adults of the Japanese beetle (*See also Biological Control and under Insect: Parasites and Predators*). —J.R.C.

BUMBLEBEE (*See under Bee*)

BUNTING
Indigo Bunting
Other Common Names—Indigo bluebird, indigo bird, indigo painted bunting, indigo finch, blue canary
Scientific Name—*Passerina cyanea*
Family—Fringillidae (grosbeaks, finches, sparrows, and buntings)
Order—Passeriformes
Size—Length, 5¼ to 5¾ inches
Range—Nests from southern New Brunswick to southern Manitoba south to southern Texas and northern Florida. It nests sporadically as far west as Colorado and Arizona. Winters from Yucatan through Central America, and in Cuba

The male indigo bunting is the smallest *all blue* bird in the eastern part of North America. It appears to be deep blue in one light, greenish-blue in another, almost black in the distant shadows. In contrast, the female is brownish without stripes or wing bars or other distinctive marks.

The indigo bunting, like other members of the Fringillidae family, has a short strong bill adapted for cracking seeds. One group in the finch family, including the cardinal, goldfinch, rose-breasted grosbeak, and indigo bunting, is bright and colorful. The other, the sparrow group, is dull and streaked.

Of the entire family, the indigo bunting seems the most exotic, as if it belonged to the tropics. It arrives late in the month of May. It enjoys the warmth of the sun, singing with hardly a stop through the heat of the July days. Its double notes—*sweet-sweet, chew-chew*—are high and strident. The indigo bunting sings its spirited song from dawn to sundown.

Each species of bird needs a certain habitat, a type of country in which it is best able to live. The indigo bunting's usual habitat is a weedy field, brushy pasture or a slashing on the hillside—a rather open place with many bushes and perhaps a few young trees.

The nest is a grass-lined cup in the

Indigo bunting

heart of a tall bush along some roadside or in an open, brushy area. The usual number of eggs is three or four. Their color is a pale bluish-white, and they take about 12 days to hatch. Like those of other songbirds, the newborn young are helpless, featherless, and blind. In a surprisingly short time they feather out and within 9 or 10 days are ready to leave the nest. They are bobtailed and husky when they make their first excursion, but hardly able to fly. They may flutter away for a few feet, then make a wild lunge for the nearest twig. Since it takes only a little over a month from the time the eggs are laid until the young can fend for themselves, indigo buntings usually raise two broods a season.

The diet of the indigo bunting is largely of insects. During the summer it will eat grasshoppers, caterpillars, plant lice, and beetles. At other times it eats weed seeds.

Late in August the male molts his bright, greenish-blue feathers and acquires the dull brown plumage worn by his mate. It seems odd that this should happen just before his journey in September to the tropics where many of the birds are brilliant. The trip is by way of Mexico to Central America. —A.B., Jr.

Lazuli buntings

Lazuli Bunting
Other Common Names—Lazuli painted finch
Scientific Name—*Passerina amoena*
Family—Fringillidae (grosbeaks, finches, sparrows, and buntings)
Order—Passeriformes
Size—Length, 5 to 5½ inches
Range—Nests from Texas to Saskatchewan and from California to British Columbia in the Far West. Winters from Baja California to southern Arizona and into Mexico

Lapis lazuli, or azure stone, is a mineral with a rich blue color. It is a deep blue shade, more like the color of the male indigo bunting. Lazuli bunting is a pretty name, but turquoise bunting, or turquoise finch, though less euphonious, would be more accurate. The lazuli bunting looks like a small bluebird. The combination of colors—blue, rust, and white—is much the same, but the lazuli has two bars of white in the wing. The rust color on the breast is just a narrow band, not so extensive as on the bluebird.

Within the United States, the lazuli bunting is a summertime bird. It comes from Mexico in late April or May. The male arrives first, stakes his territorial claim, and pours forth his song—a *sweet-sweet, chew-chew*—from the tip of a branch or a bush top. It is a typical finch song but less vigorous and emphatic than that of its eastern relative, the indigo bunting.

The brown female has just enough blue in the wings and tail to give a clue to her identity. She could easily be mistaken for some nondescript sort of sparrow.

The lazuli bunting seems to prefer dry, brushy hillsides, canyon slopes, and chaparral. Although it prefers the low, warm valleys, it sometimes follows the brushy growth to the higher levels on the mountains—even into the cool Canadian zone.

The coarsely woven, basketlike nest is built in a bush or small tree, and sometimes in the weeds. It consists of dead grasses, leaves, cocoons, and strips of bark, and is lined with finer grasses or horsehair. The nest is woven firmly into the supporting twigs. The female lays four light blue, unspotted eggs.

The young are fed caterpillars and grubs at first, and soft seeds later. By the time the young are ready to fly, their diet is about two-thirds seeds and one-third insects.

The male works as hard as his mate filling the gaping mouths, but he lets nothing interfere with his singing. The lazuli can sing even with a mouthful of insects. How he does it without dropping a caterpillar now and then is a mystery. When the young are ready to leave the nest, they are brown like their mother, but with some streaking and no blue. In most birds where the male wears the bright colors and the female the dull, the young in their juvenile plumage take after their mother.

Only a few lazuli buntings winter in the extreme southwestern corner of the United States. The majority of them move farther south into Mexico.

—A.B.,Jr.

Snow Bunting
Other Common Names—Snowflake, white snowbird
Scientific Name—*Plectrophenax nivalis*
Family—Fringillidae (grosbeaks, finches, sparrows, and buntings)
Order—Passeriformes
Size—Length, 6 to 7¼ inches
Range—Breeds in the Arctic Zone. Winters in southern Canada and the northern tier of the United States. Occasionally appears as far south as the Ohio River, northern Georgia, northern New Mexico, and northern California

Few birds have more appropriate and descriptive names than the snow bunting. Sometimes it is called *white snowbird* or *snowflake*. It thrives in heavy snows and biting winds. Polar birds must have acquired an extraordinary power of resisting cold or they could not survive.

Snow buntings are plump, compactly built, and just a little larger than the familiar house sparrow. It is difficult to see in the snow, for it is all white underneath and has much white on the neck, head, wings, and tail. The snow bunting's color is a deep rust-red, but it is so mixed with the white that even at a short distance the birds look as though they are animated leaves frolicking in the blowing snow. This is the snow bunting's winter dress; in summer it wears black and white.

The snow bunting is one of a small group of circumpolar birds whose summer home is farther north than most other landbirds, within the Arctic Circle. It nests on the barrens, north of the tree line, and on the mossy plains that skirt the arctic shores of Asia and Europe.

The snow bunting is a ground-loving bird. Not only does it nest on the ground, but spends most of its time there. After feeding, it takes shelter in a brush heap or in the edges of a "corn shock" or "stack" in an open field. This trait may

326 BUNTING

be hereditary in species that are natives of areas offering so few perching possibilities as do the treeless arctic shores. The nest of the snow bunting is built with a great quantity of short, curled grass mixed with moss that grows in the arctic regions. It is a very substantial structure, with walls an inch or more thick and a small, deep cavity (*See also under Bird: Nests and Nesting*). It is warmly lined with many waterfowl feathers, is built on the ground, often covered and hidden by tussocks of grass, or under slabs of rock. The eggs are exceedingly variable in color as well as size. They are white, or whitish, and sometimes flecked all over with neutral tint shell-markings overlaid by deep brown spots.

While his mate incubates the eggs, the male sings his simple, but sweet song—a high, clearly whistled *teer* or *tew*—at frequent intervals. He begins his song by rising high up in the air, and at the end of the strain drops suddenly to

Snow buntings

the ground. He helps feed the young by bringing beetles and other insects to the nest.

In addition, the snow bunting eats weed seeds and the minute shellfish that attach themselves to the leaves of water plants and rushes, so there is reason for the plump appearance of the bird. Upon this plumpness depends its life, for it is the layer of fat beneath its skin that enables it to endure the cold.

In winter the snow bunting moves southward into central Europe, northern China, and into the northern United States. Its southward invasions are always uncertain and irregular on both continents. —A.B., Jr.

BUSHTIT
Common Bushtit
Other Common Names—None
Scientific Name—*Psaltriparus minimus*
Family—Paridae (titmice, verdins, and bushtits)
Order—Passeriformes
Size—Length, 4 to 4½ inches
Range—Breeds all along the Pacific Coast from southern British Columbia to northern Mexico, and from Idaho, Utah, and western Wyoming to central-western Texas. Winters in same areas although there is a partial southward migration

The bushtit's home is on the Pacific Coast. Through a large part of California it forages about in flocks almost nine months of the year. It comes to Oregon and Washington in the spring, nests, and then departs in the fall.

Members of a flock of bushtits are always restless and move continually. A few always take the lead, bobbing along from tree to tree. Others follow rapidly, and when they take possession of a bush it looks as if it has suddenly sprouted wings.

The bushtit is a little larger than a hummingbird but is more fluffy in appearance, with a stubby bill and a tail as long as its body. It is gray and brown and has no distinctive color marks.

Bushtits

The bushtit has a series of call notes—frequently uttered lisps and chips—that are of great importance in keeping each member of the flock informed as to where the others are. As they bustle along, the calls are important in keeping the flock together.

When any bushtit sights a hawk nearby, all those in the flock utter a rapid twitter from within the leafy canopy—a "confusion chorus" it is called, and very useful for warning both bushtits and other birds nearby.

Throughout the western part of Oregon and Washington, bushtits often nest in willows, hemlocks, or hazels, and the site selected is usually from six to eight feet from the ground. In California the oaks are favorite nesting places. It is a masterbuilder among birds, for it constructs an impressive nest. After the pair have selected a site, they begin weaving some crosspieces between the twigs. Then they leave a place for a round entrance and begin weaving the walls out of moss, fibers, and lichens. The feather lining is added last. When the nest is finished it resembles a long pocket. In some parts of Oregon, where the moss hangs in long bunches on the limbs of trees, the bushtit utilizes this as a natural beginning for a nest.

Bushtits consume an enormous amount of insects. After the pure white eggs have hatched, both parents feed the young. They are busy from dawn until dark searching the leaves, twigs, branches, and trunks of every tree. They hunt through bushes, grasses, and ferns, bringing caterpillars, moths, scales, daddy longlegs, bark lice, and spiders back to the nest at frequent intervals.

Bushtits make a partial migration southward, although a few will winter in the area where they spend the summer or where they were born. —A.B., Jr.

BUTEO
The Broad-winged Hawks or Mouse Hawks

The hawks one most often sees are of the genus *Buteo*, a group of large soaring hawks with broad, rounded wings, and short tails that spread out like a fan. All members of this group are conspicuous because of their size, and because they are birds of the open. Their favorite perches are the tops of dead trees but they are usually seen in the air, for these hawks spend much time soaring. Hour after hour they ride the air currents with scarcely a wing motion, taking advantage of the "chimneys" of warm rising air, which on still days are often topped with fleecy "picture" clouds (*See under Bird: Bird Flight*). It is a common sight to see several hawks circling within one of these thermal currents, being carried higher and higher until they are mere specks against the sky, only to descend finally in a long slow glide to the base of another air column to circle and rise again.

This leisurely activity is more than a pastime. It is a vigilant search for food. Even from heights of several hundred feet a hawk's keen eyes can detect slight movements in the fields below. Noticing a quick scamper on the part of a small creature, very likely a mouse, the hawk makes a sudden swoop earthward, and will carry its prey aloft in sharp curved talons devouring it on a perch, or feeding it to the young birds in the nest. Mice, especially meadow mice, are a staple food of buteos—the red-tailed, broad-winged, red-shouldered, rough-legged, and Swainson's hawks. These are the so-called "mouse hawks."

Rough-legged hawk

Red-tailed hawk

Red-shouldered hawk

Broad-winged hawk

Ferruginous hawks, light phase (foreground); dark phase (rear)

And what of the mice? Meadow mice, girdlers of young trees, consumers of hay, corn, and other crops, are a highly prolific group. At the age of 25 days a meadow mouse is old enough to breed (*See under Mouse*). One pair of these mice is capable of having 17 litters a year, each averaging 5 young.

The potential offspring from one pair of meadow mice in one year's time could be well over a million mice, if one included the original breeding pair's offspring and the three following generations, assuming that all the mice survived and bred to capacity. A population of this size would require 23 million pounds of green vegetable matter to sustain it.

Fortunately no such population explosions have ever occurred, although populations of more than 250 mice per acre have been reported during mouse plagues. Meadow mice are a staple food for numerous predators such as hawks, owls, skunks, weasels, foxes, and snakes. It is in areas where these predators have been largely exterminated that mouse plagues are most apt to occur. —D.A.T.

Buteos are a widespread genus of hawks. In Europe they are known as buzzards. Many kinds also live in Asia and Africa. North America has 11 species, and, in addition, 2 other genera having 1 species each (i.e., the black hawk and Harris' hawk), that resemble buteos so closely that they are usually described with them. The 11 North American buteos are: broad-winged hawk, ferruginous hawk, gray hawk, Harlan's hawk, red-shouldered hawk, red-tailed hawk, rough-legged hawk, short-tailed hawk, Swainson's hawk, white-tailed hawk, and zone-tailed hawk.

The buteos are similar to each other in appearance and behavior, although some species show a preference for a certain type of habitat. —G.B.S.

Ferruginous Hawk
Other Common Names—Ferruginous rough-legged buzzard
Scientific Name—*Buteo regalis*
Family—Accipitridae (hawks, Old World vultures, and harriers)
Order—Falconiformes
Size—Length, 23 to 24 inches
Range—Prairie provinces of Canada and western United States

Over the open plains the large buteo with the rufous-colored back, tail, and legs and very light underparts is the ferruginous hawk. As it soars and wheels through the air, the tucked in dark legs form a distinct V against the white underparts. The tail may be all rufous, may be white at the base, or may be largely white; in the immature the tail is banded lightly. The legs do not appear dark in the immature, and the best field mark is the contrast in color between the dark back and the light underparts.

This species feeds on ground squirrels and other rodents. Inhabiting a treeless area, it often nests on cliffs and rocky hillsides. —G.B.S.

Nest and young of red-shouldered hawk

Red-shouldered hawks

Red-shouldered Hawk
Other Common Names—Red-shouldered buzzard, chicken hawk
Scientific Name—*Buteo lineatus*
Family—Accipitridae (hawks, Old World vultures, and harriers)
Order—Falconiformes
Size—Length, 18 to 24 inches
Range—From southern Nova Scotia and Quebec south to Florida, west to the plains; also on Pacific Coast

The red-shouldered hawk is only slightly smaller than the red-tailed hawk, and has shorter wings. It is more a bird of swamp woodlands than the red-tailed hawk is, and seldom occurs over the prairies. The adults and the young in the immature plumage have a patch of rufous at the bend of the wing, from which the species is named. They also have patches

332   BUTEO

Red-tailed hawk

of lighter coloration on the base of the wings. Adults can also be identified by the fine, uniform reddish banding visible on the underparts—a feature this species shares only with the smaller broad-winged hawk. Other differences between the two are that the tail is dark in the red-shouldered hawk, and there are about seven thin, light bands marked on its tail; the broad-winged hawk has fewer bands that are of equal width and that are much more strongly contrasting.

The red-shouldered hawk feeds largely on rodents, only occasionally taking an injured or unwary bird. —G.B.S.

Red-tailed Hawk
Other Common Names—Red-tailed buzzard, chicken hawk
Scientific Name—*Buteo jamaicensis*
Family—Accipitridae (hawks, Old World vultures, and harriers)
Order—Falconiformes
Size—Length, 19 to 25 inches
Range—From southern Canada through southern Alaska south into Central America; winters over much of the United States

The red-tailed hawk is a typical large buteo that lives over most of North America. Rodents and rabbits are its chief food. It nests along the edge of the forest, preferring large trees where it builds a large nest of sticks lined with dead leaves. The female lays from two to four eggs.

The best field mark of the adult bird is the red color on the *upper* surface of the tail. From below, the red may not be visible, but any other hawk of this size, except the rough-legged hawk and the ferruginous hawk, would show a banded tail. The chest is white, and the belly is streaked.

The immature bird has a finely banded tail in two tones of gray that usually appear as a solid tone, and there is no red on the upper surface of the tail. To further complicate matters, a number of races of red-tailed hawks exist, some of which are much darker than normal while others are much lighter. Also, individual birds may show a marked red, black, or even white coloring. Fortunately for sureness of their identity all red-tailed hawks have a reddish upper tail surface when adult. —G.B.S.

Rough-legged Hawk
Other Common Names—Rough-legged buzzard
Scientific Name—*Buteo lagopus*
Family—Accipitridae (hawks, Old world vultures, and Harriers)
Order—Falconiformes
Size—Length, 20 to 23 inches
Range—Circumpolar, breeding on, or at,

Rough-legged hawk

the edge of the tundra throughout the northern hemisphere; winters south to North Carolina and New Mexico

The rough-legged hawk is distinctly a northern bird, feeding almost entirely upon lemmings in the warm months and taking ground squirrels and other rodents in the winter. The hunting flight of this species is low over the ground, flapping and gliding, then hovering above a small mammal before swooping down to seize it.

The wings are long for a buteo, and the tail moderately so. The head and breast are very light, and the belly quite dark. In flight the light wing linings show a black "wrist patch" at the bend of the wing. The base of the tail is often white, but the silhouette is far too chunky and round-winged to be mistaken for a marsh hawk (See also Hawk). —G.B.S.

BUTTER-AND-EGGS
Other Common Names—Yellow toadflax
Scientific Name—*Linaria vulgaris*
Family—Scrophulariaceae (figwort family)
Range—Newfoundland to Florida
Habitat—Fields and waste places
Time of Blooming—May to first frost

This plant, like so many that grow in North American fields, was introduced from Europe.

The flowers are two-lipped, and each is perched on the top of a tubular, saclike structure called the spur that originates at the stem. The upper lip, which stands erect, consists of two lobes, and the lower lip consists of three lobes that close the throat of the tube.

This palatelike arrangement, closing the throat of the tube and doors to its honey wells, allows only the heavy insects, such as bees and bumblebees, to sip its nectar. When the bumblebee alights on the lower lip, its weight forces the throat of the flower open, and the bumblebee thus gains entrance to the flower. Once inside, the bumble-

Butter-and-eggs

bee sips the nectar contained in the long spur and, at the same time, receives a liberal dusting of pollen. These insects are the chief pollinating agents of the butter-and-eggs (*See Pollination*).

An orange-colored tuft rests on the top of the lower yellow lip, giving the flower a slight resemblance to the mouth of a toad. Thus, in some regions, butter-and-eggs has acquired the nickname, toadflax. Butter-and-eggs has also been called such names as eggs-and-bacon, impudent lawyer, Jacob's ladder, deadmen's bones, brideweed, and rabbit flower. It is interesting to note that while butter-and-eggs has been named because of the colors of the corolla, its native-born relative, *Linaria canadensis*, or the blue toadflax, is blue in appearance. Thus one might describe the blue toadflax as "blue butter-and-eggs."

The blue toadflax grows in dry, sandy soil from Nova Scotia to Florida and west to Nebraska. Its two types of flowers, blooming in summer, usually lack a corolla and it produces seeds by self-pollination. The seeds of the toadflax are small and have been carried in hay and crop seeds to many areas.

Both the butter-and-eggs and the blue toadflax are members of the figwort family, or Scrophulariaceae, of which there are 180 genera and 3,000 species widely distributed throughout the world. The wide distribution of the butter-and-eggs in all temperate regions has made it a somewhat troublesome weed in some areas. However, weeds have their uses in nature and often are "pioneering" plants on dry, sterile soil, where other plants cannot grow. —A.M.M.

Tall buttercup

BUTTERCUP
Tall Buttercup
Other Common Names—Butter-rose
Scientific Name—*Ranunculus acris*
Family—Ranunculaceae (crowfoot family)
Range—Newfoundland to Virginia, west to Missouri
Habitat—Moist fields and meadows
Time of Blooming—From April through early fall

A native of Europe, the buttercup has established itself well on North American soil. The abundant buttercup grows in pastures and meadows, and almost any place there is sufficient water. Buttercups are among the most primitive plants existing. Its flowers are characterized by an elongated axis, a large number of stamens and pistils, and a one-celled ovary. Each plant produces several bright yellow flowers. The five-petaled flowers, which open out almost flat, are about one inch in diameter. The leaves of the buttercup, or butterrose, are dark green and covered with soft hairs. Each leaf, divided into three, five, or seven parts, has deep notches around its edges. The seeds of the buttercup are contained in the center of the flower, within a hard green knot of seed vessels surrounded by many yellow stamens.

When the flower first opens, all its anthers are gathered together in the center of the stalk. The stalk bearing the anthers rises gradually until it is straightened, and the anthers then surround the pistils, thus preventing self-pollination. Beetles usually gather the nectar and pollen. Other insects, however, such as flies and bees, may be found seeking food in the bright yellow cups.

Buttercups belong to the large crowfoot family to which such flowers as columbine, marsh marigold, delphinium, hepatica, meadow rue, and clematis also belong. There are members of this family in most temperate regions of the world and in high mountain regions in the tropics; some are annuals.

Various legends have been attached to the buttercup. It was said by Pliny that eating the buttercup would cause one to go into uncontrollable fits of laughter. It was also believed that one species of the buttercup was poisonous and it was used by the ancients to poison arrows. Buttercups were used externally in the treatment of the plague.
—A.M.M.

BUTTERFLIES AND MOTHS

Butterflies and moths constitute the insect order Lepidoptera, a word that means scaly-winged. In common with some other insects, they undergo a complete metamorphosis, that is, they pass through four entirely different stages in their development: egg, larva, pupa, and adult.

How to Tell Butterflies from Moths

Many moths fly only at night while others, like the butterflies, are lovers of the sunshine. Many moths are as brightly colored as any butterfly, while some butterflies are as dull in appearance as any moth can be. Many moths fold their wings when resting, just as the butterflies do, while butterflies may rest for some time with wings outspread in the typical moth fashion. In fact, moths and butterflies are very much alike, but it is interesting to know that one can easily tell most of them apart by merely looking at the antennae, often called feelers. Butterfly antennae are slender, with a knob on the end, while those of moths lack this enlargement. Moth antennae vary considerably but many are thread-like, like those of butterflies, or look like tiny feathers.

From Egg to Adult:

The eggs of butterflies and moths must be magnified before one can readily see their beauty, for the eggs laid by our largest native moths are only about as large as the head of a pin, while the smallest cannot be seen with the naked eye. They vary greatly in shape and color.

Moths and butterflies do not incubate their eggs nor feed and protect their young as birds do. In fact, many of the adults die before the eggs hatch. However, they do provide for their young by placing the eggs on or very near the food plant that the caterpillar (larva) will feed upon—gluing the eggs to leaves of the plant as they are laid.

After the egg is laid, it takes from 1 or 2 days to perhaps 9 or 10 months to hatch, depending upon the species and the time of year. When the larva, usually called a caterpillar, is ready to emerge from the egg, it eats a hole in the shell and crawls out. Some kinds, among them the cabbage butterfly, *Pieris rapae*, then eat their shells. They soon begin feeding on the leaves of their food plant. Some kinds grow rapidly, as they must reach full size in only 10 days to a few weeks. Others, such as the Edwards' glassy-wing moth, *Hemihyalea edwardsi*, and the carpenter moth are more leisurely and take 9 or 10 months.

Few caterpillars will change their food during growth. Though caterpillars of the same species may eat several kinds of leaves, each individual prefers to eat the kind it started on.

Since a caterpillar's skin does not grow, it soon becomes too tight, whereupon the caterpillar rests for perhaps a day or two. Then the skin splits part way down the front, and the caterpillar wriggles and squirms until it is free from the old skin. However, it is not without a skin for a new and larger one has grown beneath the old. The bright new coat is often a different color from the old one. After a period of rest while the new skin dries, the caterpillar again looks for something to eat. Each caterpillar goes through this process of shedding the skin, or molting, at least four times during its growth, some as many as eight. Other species sleep all winter as caterpillars, hiding in protected places.

Hackberry butterfly on flower

When the caterpillar is full-grown, it prepares for its long rest period. If it is the larva of a moth, perhaps it will again spin a blanket of silk around itself, or it may burrow into the ground, or hide under trash and leaves on the surface of the ground. If it is to be a butterfly, it will probably spin a little silk with which to fasten its "tail," and hang with its head down, or spin an additional band of silk to support the body and help hold its head up. The spinning of the band of silk as the swallowtail and other butterfly caterpillars prepare to rest and then the formation of the cocoon is an interesting process to watch.

When this preparation is completed, the caterpillar molts once more. This time the new skin is very different from the old and soon hardens to form what is called a chrysalis case. Now, instead of being a caterpillar, it is a pupa. One would never guess it is the same creature. Its shape and color are very different. It has no eyes, mouth, or legs. But the abdominal part of the case is jointed and many wiggle violently when disturbed.

They want nothing now but to be left alone. Usually the chrysalis or cocoon is out of doors in a place where the atmosphere is not too dry.

The time spent in the chrysalis varies with the species and the time of year. Warmer weather tends to hasten the wonderful process that is going on inside the lifeless-looking shell. Most of the organs and other tissues of the caterpillar break down, turning into a semiliquid. The wings, legs, and other parts of the butterfly or moth are formed from this liquid. Many chrysalis cases are almost transparent so that one can see the change in general color as the wings and body develop.

When the adult insect is fully formed

and ready to emerge, it ejects a fluid from its mouth that softens the case so that it splits easily, allowing the creature to emerge. But if it is a moth within a cocoon, it still has something to do to free itself. A moth bumps its head repeatedly on the inside of the moistened end of the cocoon, until fibers finally give way. The moth then crawls out and up a nearby stem. Wet and bedraggled-looking, it has a large, flabby body and small stumps of wings. Gradually it pumps fluid from its body out into the wings until they have expanded to their normal size, and the body has become smaller. This requires an hour or two and, in the meantime, the scales have dried so that the wings and body are beautifully soft and fluffy. It rests a while longer, opening and closing its wings until they become hardened, then it is ready to fly away.

The most conspicuous part of a moth or butterfly are the wings. There are four of them, covered with minute scales that overlap much as shingles overlap on the roof of a house. These scales contain the coloring pigments. The scales are arranged in beautiful patterns, but they rub off on one's fingers very easily if handled too much. Two wings are attached to either side of that portion of the body called the thorax. To the under side of the thorax are attached three pairs of long, slender, jointed legs. In front of the thorax is the head. There is a large compound eye on each side of the head. The two antennae, which many authorities believe are the organs of both scent and hearing, project from the front of the head. Beneath the head is a coil that resembles a watch spring. It is a drinking tube, called a proboscis. The butterfly can straighten this out at will and it is the means by which the creature sips nectar from the flowers. Some of the large silk moths are without a proboscis and have no means of taking nourishment in the adult stage. They can live only a week or two after emerging from their cocoons. The third and longer portion of the body is the abdomen at the back of the thorax. Along either side of the abdomen is a row of nine spiracles, or breathing holes, so tiny they are not likely to be seen. At the hind end of the abdomen are the genital organs.

Relation to other Living Things

If all the eggs laid by butterflies and moths developed into mature insects, the country would soon be overrun by them, but nature has provided various controls that limit their numbers. As it is, some species have become so numerous as to destroy crops. In many instances their numbers are the fault of man, who has made the land untenable for the birds and other animals that would normally have devoured great quantities of the caterpillars. Caterpillars are an important food for many birds and mammals. Spiders help to keep some kinds in check. And then there are the parasites, several species of small flies and wasps that lay their eggs on or in the body of the caterpillar. The parasite larva hatches, burrows into the caterpillar, and feeds on its tissues (*See Insect: Predators and Parasites; also Parasite*). Sometimes the caterpillar dies before reaching full size, and sometimes it forms its cocoon or chrysalis in an apparently normal manner but, instead of a butterfly or moth, only one or more parasitic flies or wasps will emerge. Farmers have found that these parasites, where sufficiently numerous, are better than dusting with insecticides as a means of controlling destructive caterpillars (*See Biological Control*).

Not all butterflies and moths are necessarily harmful to agriculture. Many kinds are not numerous enough to do any appreciable damage because their natural enemies keep them in check. Many species eat unwanted weeds. It is the caterpillars that eat the leaves of growing plants; adult butterflies and moths

Monarch butterfly

have no means of chewing and can only sip nectar from the flowers and the juices of damaged fruit.

As the adults visit the flowers in search of nectar, they rub against the stamens and pistils, aiding in the process of pollination (*See Pollination*). The little pronuba moth is especially important in this respect, being the only means by which the blossoms of the beautiful desert yuccas are fertilized. This moth deliberately gathers a large ball of pollen, then hunts for a flower that has just bloomed and stuffs the pollen into the opening in the pistil. The moth then deposits an egg or two in the seed cup of the flower, where the larva can feed upon the developing seeds. But some seeds are always left to mature, to produce more yucca plants.

All living things are protected from their enemies in many different ways. Among butterflies and moths their coloring is their chief method of protection. It is difficult to see an angle-wing butterfly when it is at rest because, with its wings folded, it is almost indistinguishable from the bark of a tree. Some of the sphinx moths (or hawkmoths) and others look very much like dry leaves when their wings are folded. Other species resemble a daub of mud. And then there

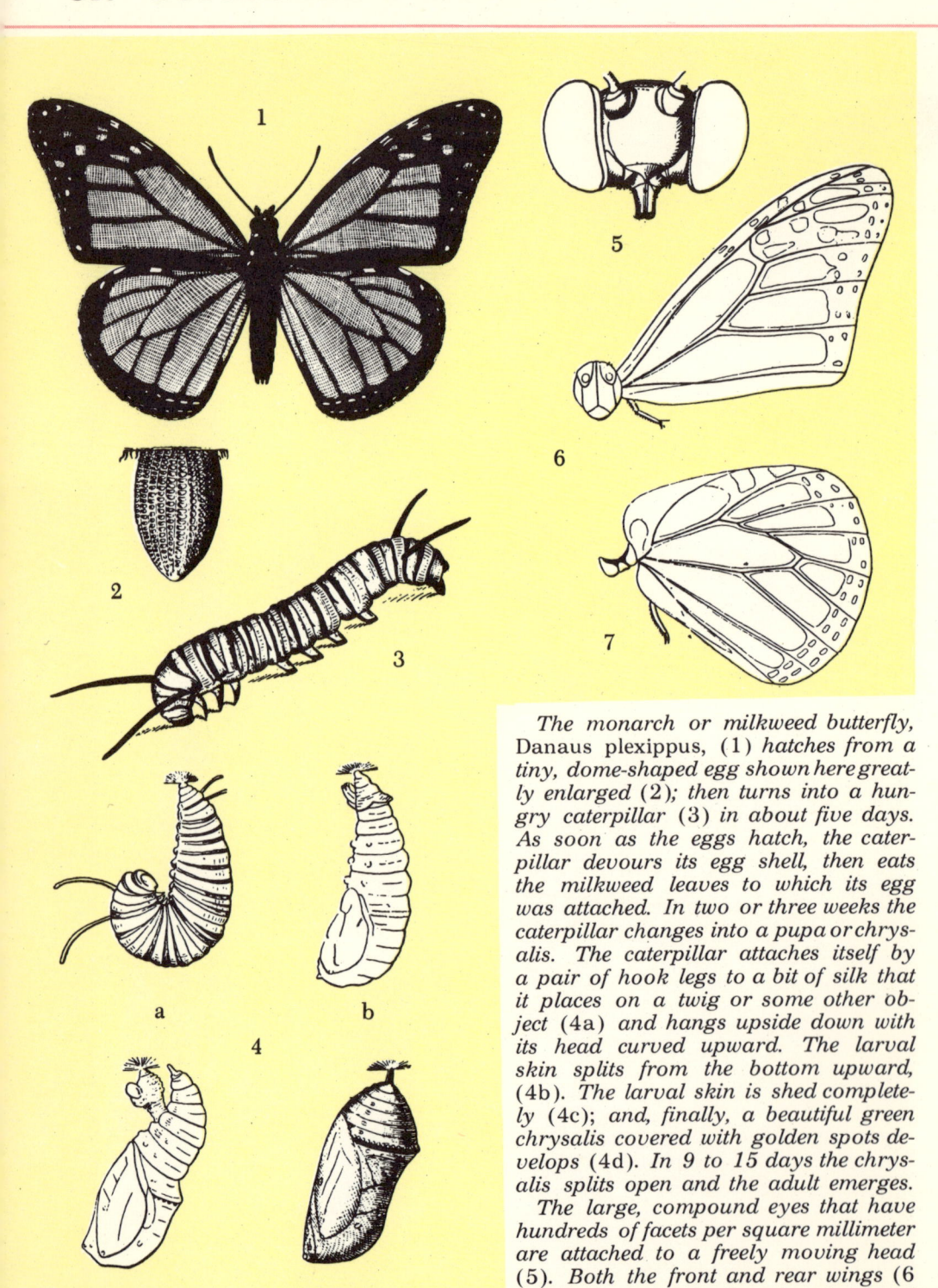

340 BUTTERFLIES AND MOTHS

The monarch or milkweed butterfly, Danaus plexippus, (1) *hatches from a tiny, dome-shaped egg shown here greatly enlarged (2); then turns into a hungry caterpillar (3) in about five days.* As soon as the eggs hatch, the caterpillar devours its egg shell, then eats the milkweed leaves to which its egg was attached. In two or three weeks the caterpillar changes into a pupa or chrysalis. The caterpillar attaches itself by a pair of hook legs to a bit of silk that it places on a twig or some other object (4a) *and hangs upside down with its head curved upward. The larval skin splits from the bottom upward,* (4b). *The larval skin is shed completely (4c); and, finally, a beautiful green chrysalis covered with golden spots develops (4d).* In 9 to 15 days the chrysalis splits open and the adult emerges.

The large, compound eyes that have hundreds of facets per square millimeter are attached to a freely moving head (5). *Both the front and rear wings (6 and 7) are well developed and covered with tiny scales.*

BUTTERFLIES AND MOTHS 341

is the leaf butterfly of the tropics that resembles a leaf when at rest.

Where do they spend the cold winter months? Most moths and butterflies live only a few weeks as adults. Their progeny usually survive the winter as an egg, caterpillar, chrysalis, or cocoon, but the mourning cloak butterfly, *Aglais antiopa*, and some of its relatives seek out a protected place and go to sleep. Several feet of snow may cover their cozy shelter but, with the warmth of spring, they awaken once more to hunt for food and to lay their eggs. Most butterflies and moths lay their eggs soon after emerging from the chrysalis, but the mourning cloak doesn't follow this rule.

In Canada great swarms of monarch butterflies gather in the fall and fly to southern locations where food is plentiful all winter. There they congregate in certain trees, foraging over the countryside during the day (*See Butterfly Migration*). Other species, such as some of the tortoise shells and painted ladies, sometimes fly in swarms, especially when their food plants have become scarce, but they do not migrate with the unfailing regularity of the monarch.

A flower garden is the best means of attracting butterflies. Among the flowers they like especially are candytuft, zinnia, coral bell, valerian, and buddleia (butterfly bush or summer lilac). Boysenberry blossoms also attract them. Often butterflies will flock to a wet spot along a garden path, especially in hot weather. Where it is not possible to plant a garden, even a few flowering plants in pots may attract them. Some butterflies are attracted to garbage dumps, spoiling fruit, and other refuse.

The large, bright green caterpillar (2) of the American silk worm, Telea polyphemus, *after eating 86,000 times its own weight in 56 days, constructs a silken cocoon that it covers with leaves (3). The pupa (4) remains motionless for about nine months before it secretes a special acid that allows it to escape from its cocoon without breaking a single silk fiber. The adult (1) appears usually in May, but hatching time varies with the temperature.*

Recommended Reading

The Butterfly Book—W. J. Holland. Doubleday & Company, Inc., New York.
Butterflies of California—J. A. Comstock. Published by the author. Southern California Academy of Sciences, Exposition Park, Los Angeles.
Field Book of Insects—Frank E. Lutz. G. P. Putnam's Sons, New York.
A Field Guide to the Butterflies—A. B. Klots. Houghton Mifflin Company, Boston.

342 BUTTERFLIES AND MOTHS

Dog-face
Red-spotted purple
Baltimore
Buckeye
Banded purple
Question mark
Black swallowtail
Tailed blue
Pipevine swallowtail

Butterflies

Imported cabbage-worm
Red admiral
Zebra swallowtail
Melissa blue

Tiger swallow-tail
Compton tortoise shell
Common sulphur — male
Common sulphur — female
Long tailed skipper
Frosted skipper

Little wood-satyr
Mourning cloak
Monarch
Viceroy

American copper
Giant swallowtail

Regal silverspot
Great spangled silverspot
Wood nymph
Spice bush swallowtail

BUTTERFLIES AND MOTHS 343

Regal

Satellite sphinx

Gypsy—female

Polyphemus

Gypsy—male

White-lined sphinx

Cynthia

and

Moths

Tiger

White underwing

Black witch

Modest sphinx

Imperial

Promethea —male above female

Luna

Buck

Tomato hornworm sphinx

Clear wing sphinx

Achemon sphinx

Cecropia

Io—male above female

Briseis underwing

Twin-spot sphinx

Red-spotted purple butterfly

Butterfly Migration

Some years ago C. C. Williams, the British entomologist, listed more than 250 insects that migrate. The most famous of them all is the monarch, or milkweed butterfly, *Danaus plexippus*. Its drifting movement to the south, in the early days of autumn, is a feature of every North American fall. Over hundreds of miles—2,000 miles and more in some cases—the journeying butterflies move like migrating birds down the map of North America. Instinctively holding to their course, they keep on for days and weeks while the trees around them change from spruce and apple to cypress and the moss-hung live oaks of the Gulf Coast or the palms and orange trees of the Florida peninsula.

Monarchs drift down the Long Island shore—sometimes a thousand individuals an hour fluttering past the dunes. They cluster on Spanish oaks at Cape May, New Jersey, when the autumn birds are going through. They also move south along the ridges of Hawk Mountain in Pennsylvania at a time of the migration of the broadwings and sharpshins. But the full magnitude of this annual insect migration cannot be fully appreciated until a person crosses North America from Cape Cod to California in the fall of the year. Those weeks of travel reveal in nationwide cross section the southward-bound hordes of butterflies.

Monarchs flutter over the sand of Provincetown and Monomoy on Cape Cod. They drift south across the flatlands of Ohio. They cross the wild Au Sable River in northern Michigan and migrate down the Mississippi. They move along the mountains of Nevada and even cross the shimmering white desert of the salt flats in Utah. And down the Pacific Coast, past Douglas firs and the spires of the redwoods, over the matted salal and sea figs of the shore, other monarchs drift toward their winter home among the Monterey pines at Pacific Grove, California. Moving across the continent the butterflies sweep in a steady insect tide toward the south.

The place where this annual movement receives most attention is at Pacific Grove. This community overlooks Monterey Bay on the California coast. The whole town is a refuge for monarchs. It is one of the few insect sanctuaries in the world.

An ordinance passed by the city council on November 16, 1938 proclaims: "Inasmuch as the monarch butterflies are a distinct asset to the City of Pacific Grove, and cause innumerable people to visit said city each year to see the said butterflies, it is the duty of the citizens of said city to protect the butterflies in every way possible from serious harm and possible extinction by brutal and heartless people." A fine up to $500 and a jail sentence of up to six months are provided for those who molest or harm the butterflies. The monarch is on the seal of the Chamber of Commerce of Pacific Grove, signs along the street guide visitors to the butterfly trees, and every year school children, dressed as monarchs and other species, march down the main street of the town in a butterfly parade.

Year after year the monarchs return to the same high pines overlooking the sea. It is estimated that as many as two million butterflies spend the winter at Pacific Grove, concentrated within an area of only a few acres. To this identical spot their ancestors have come each autumn—for how many years, no man knows. The Monterey pines rise high, their branches dripping with the gray lichen that resembles Spanish moss, the lichen, *Ramalina reticulata*. In masses and festoons on the branches, clinging to the twigs, to the needles, to the pendant lichen, are thousands—tens of thousands—of monarchs. With wings closed, they pack together like gray-brown leaves.

A few of the butterflies fly about but the great mass of the monarchs remain quiescent. They are settled in their winter home. For days at a time they cling in the same spot. They are not hibernating; they are only semidormant. A few at a time leave the clustered masses and drift away in search of nectar. But most of them cling unmoving to the trees of this ancestral wintering ground. None of these same monarchs has been to Pacific Grove before, for no monarch makes the fall migration a second time. Its life cycle is too short to bridge the gap from autumn to autumn. Instinctively, without leaders, the butterflies return year after year to the very trees where past generations have found sanctuary and a winter home.

Those who have watched the migrants arrive tell of long trailing clouds of butterflies streaming across the bay. One observer describes the progress of the insects as looking like an undulating, colorful oriental rug. It is usually around the middle of October when the monarchs come to Pacific Grove; it is March when they leave. One of the odd local beliefs about this massing of butterflies is the idea that the insects come to suck the sap of the lichen and, in consequence, spend the winter in an intoxicated stupor.

Although the region has long been settled, and Monterey—only a mile or so away—was the capital of California in the old Spanish days, this phenomenon of the wintering butterflies was not closely observed until Lucia Shepardson, then a resident of Pacific Grove, began studying it in 1907.

No one can walk among the insect-laden pines or contemplate the long, instinct-guided journey of the butterflies without raising several questions. Why does this particular spot attract the monarchs? How do they recognize the identical trees that supported their ancestors during the winter months of other years? How do they find their way to Pacific Grove? Why do they stop here instead of continuing southward?

On the Monterey peninsula there are other, smaller concentrations; but the great assemblage, year after year, is located in the same pines in the same grove. It is North America's most spectacular concentration of these butterflies. East of the Rockies the autumn migration scatters the monarchs over wide areas along the Gulf of Mexico. They are sometimes seen in immense numbers in the swamps of Louisiana, on the Texas coast, and in Florida, especially in the region of Apalachicola. But it is believed that nowhere else do they spend the winter in such numbers in one spot, returning to the same trees and branches annually, as they do at Pacific Grove.

However, the long autumn flight of the monarchs elsewhere presents other and perhaps even more puzzling problems. It might be said that the butterflies reach Pacific Grove simply by following the coastline south. But what of the monarchs flying across Kansas or Ohio, winging their way over hundreds of miles of plains and woods, flat land that stretches away to the horizon? No river or coastline guides them. How do they hold to a southward course day after day?

On four-inch wings these migrants journey from the Canadian border to the Gulf of Mexico, and often farther, all the while traversing country they have never seen before. Because one monarch looks like another monarch, people see them in the mass. The manner in which the millions of butterflies stream southward is known. But what happens to the individual—its adventures along the way, its destination, its winter life, its northward movement when spring returns?

When John James Audubon placed a silver wire on the leg of a phoebe and thus identified it beyond doubt when it returned in spring to its Pennsylvania nesting place, birdbanding was initiated in America. By the use of lightweight, numbered bands students in many parts of the country have aided in the discovery of facts about the movement of

A monarch butterfly marked with aniline dye that will help trace its wanderings (note the dark cross-shaped mark on upper wing)

birds that could have been ascertained in no other way. The banding of butterflies is not possible, but marking them in some other way, so the individual can be identified later, is the only key that will unlock the riddles of their seasonal movements north and south.

Many ideas for accomplishing this have been suggested. For a number of years C.A. Anderson, an Internal Revenue official at Dallas, Texas, "branded" butterflies. He used a rubber stamp and special check-protection ink to place a number on the wing of each monarch before it was liberated. In other parts of the country the butterflies have been caught and marked with daubs of aniline dye. Stickers were pasted on the wings of monarchs in other experiments. Unfortunately they soon came off. At the Royal Ontario Museum of Zoology and Paleontology, in Toronto, Canada, still another scheme was tested. A small hole was punched in the fore wing just behind the strong leading rib and a lightweight paper label, carrying the return address was folded over the wing so that the paper was glued to itself through the hole.

Most of the ideas for marking monarchs, such as the above, require individual handling of the insects. Frank E. Lutz, when head of the Department of Insects and Spiders at the American Museum of Natural History in New York City, suggested a method of wholesale marking. His plan was to spray aniline dye over the thousands of insects massed at a butterfly tree, thus marking them all in a single operation. It may even be possible, in this Atomic Age, to mark monarchs with material containing isotopes and then to identify the insects later at points of concentration by means of Geiger counters. Something of the kind has already been tried successfully in laboratory experiments with caterpillars and other living creatures.

The difficulty of obtaining information about the travels of marked butterflies

Monarch butterflies feed on their food plant, the milkweed

is obvious. The monarchs are so many, the areas they traverse so vast, the individuals that can be marked so relatively few, the chances of their being seen among all the millions of journeying butterflies so slight, that only large-scale and persistent efforts will have any chance of success.

Of 3,000 monarchs marked at one butterfly tree in Ontario, only 7 were seen later; 2,993—or 99.2 percent—were never heard of again. Still, it is encouraging to note that at no previous time in history has so much attention by so many people been directed toward solving the mysteries that surround the life of the monarch.

Life for the monarch begins in a jewel-like, pointed, pale green egg that is laid usually close to one of the ribs on the underside of a milkweed leaf. The monarch is well nicknamed the milkweed butterfly. The caterpillar that hatches from the egg—a midget hardly an eighth of an inch long—is ravenous for only one food—the juicy tissues of the milkweed plant.

Occasionally a larva will be found on dogbane, but this is extremely rare. It is milkweed leaves that the immature monarch craves. When it reaches full size and becomes a striking caterpillar with transverse bands of black and white and yellow, it attaches itself by its tail and transforms into a chrysalis. This pupa is a beautiful waxy green, decorated with spots that look like burnished gold.

A dozen days usually pass before the winged adult appears, but the time varies greatly, depending upon weather conditions. Sometimes the transformation is completed in three or four days; at other times, especially during dry spells, the pupal stage may be prolonged to nearly three weeks. Because the butterflies sometimes emerge just before a rainstorm on summer days, one common name bestowed on the monarch is the storm fritillary.

Still another name, the *wanderer*, is merited by the far-ranging life of the adult. The monarch is a strong flier. It flaps and glides in calm and moderate winds, sailing in easy flight with a minimum of effort. But facing a stiff breeze, it beats its wings steadily and thus forces its way ahead into winds sufficiently strong to set the branches of small trees tossing.

During migration the insects fly with a quartering wind or a side wind or with the wind dead ahead, as well as through calms and barely moving breezes. At Point Pelee on the shore of Lake Ontario, a steady stream of migrating monarchs was once observed heading out across the waves directly into a wind that was sweeping over the water at what seemed scarcely less than 20 miles an hour. The migrant butterflies seemed hardly moving but gradually they grew smaller as they forged ahead.

Monarchs that follow the south shore of Long Island often launch out over the ocean water, coming to land again along the New Jersey coast. Some years ago *The New York Times* reported that people in one resort community there were puzzled by this appearance of monarchs from offshore because, as they put it, "there wasn't anything out there for the caterpillars to eat."

Ships have sometimes overtaken monarchs flying strongly 500 miles at sea. Carried by ships or riding favorable winds they even reach Europe. On the west coast of Great Britain monarchs have been observed flying in from the open Atlantic. Neither in England nor on the Continent have the monarchs established themselves, however, because there is no milkweed there to support them. But as milkweed has been introduced accidentally into the islands of the Pacific, the butterflies have spread westward to Hawaii, the Philippines, Java, Sumatra, New Zealand, and Australia. It is thought likely that the insects traveled as chrysalises attached to packing material in the holds of ships.

The monarch is a New World insect, originally found only in North and South America. Its range, in all forms, extends from Nova Scotia and British Columbia to Argentina.

During the summer the monarchs drift widely. There may be as many as three or four generations in a season, and breeding experiments indicate that it is the last generation that forms the bulk of the migrants. As summer approaches fall, the butterflies become more social, begin to gather into small groups and loose flocks, their numbers swell and the southward movement begins. Do these smaller flocks tend to stay together during the long migration? Does an individual butterfly or a group of monarchs tend to migrate to the same place in the South that formed the winter home of its ancestors? One can guess at the answers but no one can be positive until the evidence provided by many marked individuals is available.

Down the pathway of the migrant monarchs certain trees, year after year, are chosen as resting places or way stations by the traveling butterflies. None of the insects has ever seen these trees before, yet they mass themselves on the same branches, generation after generation, autumn migration after autumn migration. One hundred monarchs were once counted clinging to a twig only one foot long on such a butterfly tree on Long Island. What attracts successive waves of migrants to these identical trees? Are the twigs and branches impregnated by the peculiar perfume characteristic of the male monarchs? Does this perfume help hold the ragged flocks together during their long southward movement in the fall?

Sometimes stragglers drift about in the

Monarch butterflies, sleeping or semi-dormant, cling to trees in great numbers. Butterfly Park, California is a good place to see this phenomenon

September dusk a quarter of a mile downwind from a butterfly tree where thousands of migrating monarchs have congregated for the night. As they come in line with the tree, the butterflies make a sudden turn and head directly upwind toward the tree as though following a stream of scent to its source.

Spectacular as the massed southern movement of the butterflies may be, it is the thin, scattered return journey that presents the most puzzles. Only a few of the millions of monarchs that streamed south in the fall come north in the spring. They come singly instead of in concentrations, and they are weatherworn and tarnished, less likely to catch the eye. Are most of them females? Do they travel far or only short distances into the north? Are the northern areas repopulated by migrants that left the areas in fall or by a new generation of butterflies? Do the spring monarchs make a single long reverse migration or does the northward movement take place in a series of waves?

In other words, do the butterflies stop and lay eggs part way up the map, producing a new generation that, in turn, travels instinctively northward in a kind of relay race of migration? Some scientists believe that the monarchs that reach the upper limits of their range may be the second or third generation on the northward journey. This, like so many other mysteries concerning the life of this familiar black-and-orange insect, will remain obscure until it is illuminated by evidence that only the wholesale marking of monarchs can produce.

In their continental wanderings and massed concentrations these butterflies are aided by the fact that they are usually unpalatable to birds. On rare occasions birds will eat monarchs. John W. Aldrich once saw a red-tailed hawk, which was soaring down the Kittatinny Ridge of the Appalachian Mountains, reach out with one foot, grasp a migrating monarch, strip away the wings, and eat the insect. Maurice Brooks reported seeing a starling eat a monarch. But, in the main, monarch butterflies are ignored or avoided by birds.

In the life of this common butterfly there still remains a very large chapter of things we do not yet sufficiently know. Most puzzling of all is its amazing sense of orientation. How does it find its way? Migrating monarchs approach obstructions, such as buildings or clumps of trees, and invariably rise and pass over them instead of going around them. They seem set on a compass course. But what is the compass they use? It has been suggested, just as it has in the case of migrating birds, that perhaps they are sensitive to the

Signs at the entrance to Butterfly Lane point toward the California grove where myriads of monarch butterflies spend the winter

electromagnetic lines of force that run north and south on the earth, that they use them as invisible pathways in their travels. But no organ in the insect has been shown to be sensitive to such electromagnetic lines of force and no experiments have brought forth any proof of this hypothesis.

Another possibility has been suggested by the researches of Karl Von Frisch, the famous discoverer of the "language of the bees." During his visit to America in 1949 he was working on a new series of experiments employing polaroid screens. They revealed a fact hitherto unknown—that honeybees are able to orient themselves by means of polarized light that varies in different parts of the sky. More recent studies have shown that some ants have the same ability. Perhaps the monarchs, on their long flight north and south, similarly chart their course with polarized light.

The proof or refutation of this hypothesis probably lies with trained scientists. But every bird watcher, amateur naturalist, or observing person who goes afield in spring and fall can play a part in amassing information that will give a clearer picture of the activity of this familiar and mysterious insect. Such a simple thing as recording the exact direction monarchs are seen flying would prove helpful. Multiplied many times, covering different years and different sections of the country, such records would reveal the streams and currents in the tide of monarch migration about which so little is known.

Connie Hagar, famous for her bird studies at Rockport on the Texas coast, reported that the monarchs appear in great numbers there late in October. They stay about two weeks and then virtually disappear. Where do they go? There are similar problems awaiting solution in many parts of the country.

Because birdwatchers throughout the United States are in the field during migration time, they can be especially helpful in gathering information on the movement of the monarchs. They can record the direction of flight. They can make notes on the activity of the insects. They can locate butterfly trees and other points of concentration. They can watch for marked insects and report their discovery. Like the Christmas Census and the observation of birds migrating across the moon, monarch research will be most effective if it is a cooperative venture. Over the years, such monarch-watching as a by-product of birdwatching would contribute greatly toward reducing the number of "things we do not yet sufficiently know" in the lives of these journeying butterflies.

—E.W.T.

CACTUS

These are plants that have adapted to the harsh conditions existing in arid country and burning desert. Cacti (or cactuses) belong to the family Cactacae, and are native to the western hemisphere, though some species have become naturalized in Europe, Africa, and Australia. One genus, *Pereskia*, is shrubby and has leaves, the only member of the cacti to have them, with the exception of a few forms in which the leaves are small and temporary. Spines are characteristic of the cacti. They protect the plants against animals and, if thick enough, shade the stem.

Again with the exception of the pereskias, the stems of the cacti show several modifications useful for storing water. The skin of the plant is thick and leathery, and encloses a mass of spongy inner tissue that is normally swollen with water. During long periods of dry weather when the plant uses up its water, the entire plant may shrivel, since it depends upon the tightly filled cells to remain upright.

The most widespread group of cacti in North America are the prickly pears, which have a number of species that grow from New England to Guatemala. The stems of the prickly pear are near-oval in shape, flat, and jointed. Most species have long spines. The flowers are red-orange or yellow and the fruit is edible.

Cacti that are members of the cereus group have long cylindrical stems that are heavily ribbed. Some species are climbers that need the support of trees or rocks, while others stand erect. The night-blooming cereus belong to this group.

Some cacti are entirely epiphytic; that is, they live in trees and derive their nourishment from chemicals in the air and in rainwater. Most of these grow in Central and South America.

Cacti of the barrel type have only one short stem which is very thick and rounded. Leaf cacti have flattened, leaf-shaped stems. Some of the species belonging to this group are also known as orchid cactus because of their large red or white flowers.

Many cacti grow in the drier regions of the Southwest. Forests of organ pipe, senita, and cholla cactus grow in the blazing heat. Other plants that do not belong to the cacti and are often confused with them include the yuccas, the Joshua tree, and the ocotillo. Like the cacti, each of these species has modifications that enable it to survive under conditions that would prove fatal to most plants. —G.B.S.

Beavertail Cactus
Other Common Names — Prickly pear
Scientific Name — *Opuntia basilaris*
Family — Cactaceae (cactus family)
Range — Southern Utah to Mexico
Habitat — Southwestern semiarid and arid desert
Time of Blooming — April to June

Giant Cacti

Saguaro cactus (an Indian name pronounced sah-WAH-roe) is the best known of the giant cacti, probably because it has a greater range in the United States than its cousins, the organ-pipe cactus and the senita cactus. Saguaros grow as far as 200 miles north of the Mexican border and they are rather widely distributed across southern Arizona and along the Colorado River in

Beaver tail cacti, or prickly pears, have large, waxy blossoms

California. Organ-pipe and senita cacti, on the other hand, are strictly limited in the United States to the region around Organ Pipe Cactus National Monument, in Arizona. It has been estimated that no more than 50 senita plants grow north of the Mexican border.

The larger saguaros must have been seedlings at the time Thomas Jefferson drafted the Declaration of Independence. Despite their long lives the giant cacti stand small chance against modern civilization. Around Tucson the cactus forests are waning; the giants are dying and only a tiny percentage of the seeds produced ever sprout. Rodents and ants climb the thorny stems to harvest the pinhead seeds from the fruit that crowns the branch tips, and white-winged doves depend on them so much that their range is almost identical with that of the cactus.

Saguaro fruit, and that of the organ-pipe cactus also, was a vital food source for Papago Indians until recent years. Their calendar begins in July with Navaita—"time of ripe cactus fruit." Women used to knock the fruit down with long poles and gather it into baskets. Seeds were then separated from the pulp and ground into an oily, nutritious meal. The pulp was dried and stored for future use and the juice was carefully saved; some was fermented into wine and used in rainmaking ceremonies, while the remainder was boiled down into syrup and sealed in pottery jars. Nearly all adult Papagos remember the days when the tribe camped at family owned cactus plots for the annual harvest, but few bother with it nowadays. Some fruit is eaten fresh and a few pounds are made into seedy jam, similar to fig jam.

Mostly, however, man's effect on cactus reproduction is more subtle than direct consumption of the seeds. Man makes war on the coyotes, which has resulted in an increase in the number of rodents that feed on saguaro seeds. Man allows his cattle to graze among the cacti, and their hooves trample young plants. Even cutting wood for fence posts and fireplaces has an effect. Cactus seedlings are very particular about where they grow; they must begin life in the shade of a bush or tree.

Saguaros are extremely slow-growing. It takes two years for seedlings to grow a quarter-inch high; in 30 years they are only about 3 feet tall. After that they grow 3 or 4 inches annually until they reach heights averaging 30 to 40 feet. In 60 or 70 years, prickly, round balls ap-

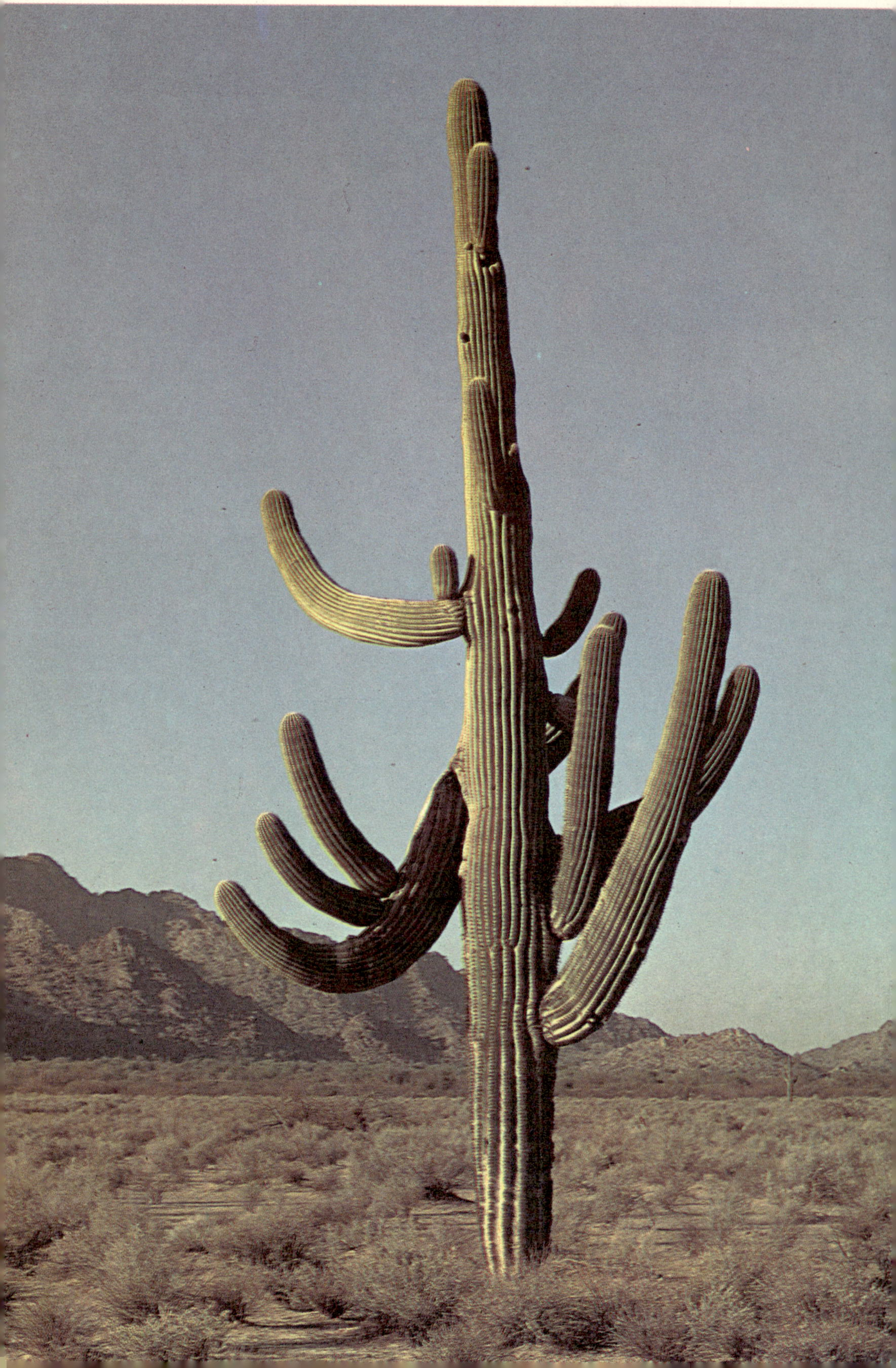

Tree chollas bear spines capable of penetrating shoe leather

pear near the tops of the plants. These are branch buds. The branches grow at the same rate as the trunk. In time, most saguaros have from two to eight arms reaching skyward—or, once in a while, drooping earthward.

The flower of the saguaro is the state flower of Arizona. Blooming takes place in the heat of June. Creamy-petaled, yellow-centered flowers crown the tips of trunks and branches. Each blossom lasts only one day, opening at night and wilting by the following afternoon. Each plant has so many buds, however, that its blooming period lasts several weeks. By July the cactus tops are crowded with ripening fruit. The fruiting is far more colorful than the flowering. As they ripen, fruits split open, revealing crimson pulp studded with thousands of shiny black seeds.

Saguaros have developed means of getting along in their difficult desert environment. Foremost, unquestionably, is their phenomenal capacity to store water. A saguaro may weigh as much as eight tons—95 percent of it water. Its spongy "watermelon tissue" is vital; with it the plants can withstand drought, drawing upon their inner reservoirs in order to flower and fruit. A shallow root system radiating 50 feet from the trunk permits the saguaros to soak up rain as quickly as it falls. Roots are fleshy and partially deciduous. New runners finger out whenever there is work to be done but they drop off when no moisture is available, leaving the minimum number of roots necessary to support the plant.

Desert rains are exciting. They usually come as hard-driven summer cloudbursts. Plants respond immediately. Many send out new leaves, others ambitiously sprout or start to flower, but saguaros just get fat. Their roots suck up water and the cacti swell, their fluted sides smoothing out. Occasionally, a saguaro will burst open from absorbing too much water. Such splits usually heal without seriously hurting the plant.

Once water is absorbed, desert plants must struggle to keep from losing it to the dry atmosphere. Some have tiny leaves that cannot possibly give off much water; others drop their foliage in dry weather. Saguaros have no leaves at all. In their place they have developed a waxy skin that does the food-making work of leaves (photosynthesis) without risking the loss of water because of transpiration.

Even the thorns of the saguaro help adapt it to desert life. Their sharpness probably offers protection from would-be molesters but, more important, they protect the plant from the sun and drying winds. Two or three inches long and growing thick on the vertical ridges, the thorns shade about one-fifth of the saguaro at a time and they break up hot air currents that otherwise would tend to dry and shrivel the plant.

The only known cause of death, other than being blown over during a windstorm, is a bacterial necrosis. First symptoms are light-colored "sores" on the skin of the cacti. These grow, turn purplish, and begin to ooze a dark sticky liquid. The plants' only means of stopping the creeping death is to wall off the rotting area with layer upon layer of a sort of cork, thus separating diseased tissue from healthy tissue.

The process is a good example of the interdependence of nature. The disease-causing bacteria are carried by a tan moth, *Cactobrosis fernaldialis*. Cactobro-

Organ-pipe catus

sis larvae feed on saguaro pulp, eating out tunnels a quarter-inch wide and yards long. Bacteria in the larvae's intestinal tracts infect the saguaro and soon disease splotches show up on the cactus skin. These splotches attract gilded flickers and Gila woodpeckers that like to eat the larvae. They dig in to get them and, of course, in doing that they clean out a lot of the rot. That helps the saguaro curb the spread of the necrosis. The saguaro then grows firm, smooth-walled tissue over the former disease pockets, which in turn make fine homes for nesting woodpeckers and elf owls. The hollows often measure four or five inches across and a foot deep.

Saguaro National Monument, 17 miles east of Tucson, Arizona, was set aside March 1, 1933, to preserve its many fine saguaros. Previous to its establishment as a national monument, the 63,000-acre tract was grazed by livestock which destroyed the young saguaros that ordinarily replace the aged ones. Organ Pipe Cactus National Monument, 330,690 acres, was established April 13, 1937.

Organ-pipe cactus, senita, and saguaro are all members of the Cereus tribe, but organ-pipe cacti and senitas look very different from saguaros. They grow only about half as high and branch at ground level from a common base rather than high up upon a central stalk. They ordinarily have 15 to 20 arms; the record is an Abra Valley senita that had 134 arms.

Like the saguaro, senita and organ-pipe cacti are vertically fluted but, instead of being supported by rib poles, organ pipes and senitas have woody pipelike cores. In a country where wood is scarce the cacti skeletons are put to good use. Mexicans and Papagos use saguaro ribs for fences and as frameworks for their adobe-plastered houses.

Another cactus classed as a giant is the tree cholla. Cholla is armored with slender thorns an inch and a half long and covered with straw-colored, papery sheaths that deceive the unwary by glowing in the sunlight. The spines are barbed and it is as painful to remove them from oneself as to be pricked by them.

Tree chollas commonly grow 6 to 10 feet high though some reach 20 feet in height. They have a dark trunk that branches a foot or two above the ground, forming a tree-shaped plant. Cylindrical prickly lobes cluster thick on the branches, and chains of fruit hang weeping-willow style. —R.K.

CADDISFLY

North America has 17 genera and about 200 species of caddisflies, members of the order Trichoptera. They are closely related to the moths, but the adults differ from moths in having a short, uncoiled proboscis and longer antennae. They are poor fliers; the wings, under the microscope, are usually hairy.

The aquatic larvae of the caddisfly are possibly of greater interest than the adults. The female lays as many as 1,000 eggs at a time at the edge of ponds or streams. When they hatch, the wormlike larvae crawl to the bottom of the pond and build body-protective cases under rocks or logs in which to mature. Each species builds a different kind of case. With some it is made entirely of silk; with others the silk is covered by grains of sand, tiny bits of plant stem, or even small snail shells—all of which are glued by the larva to the outer surface of its case.

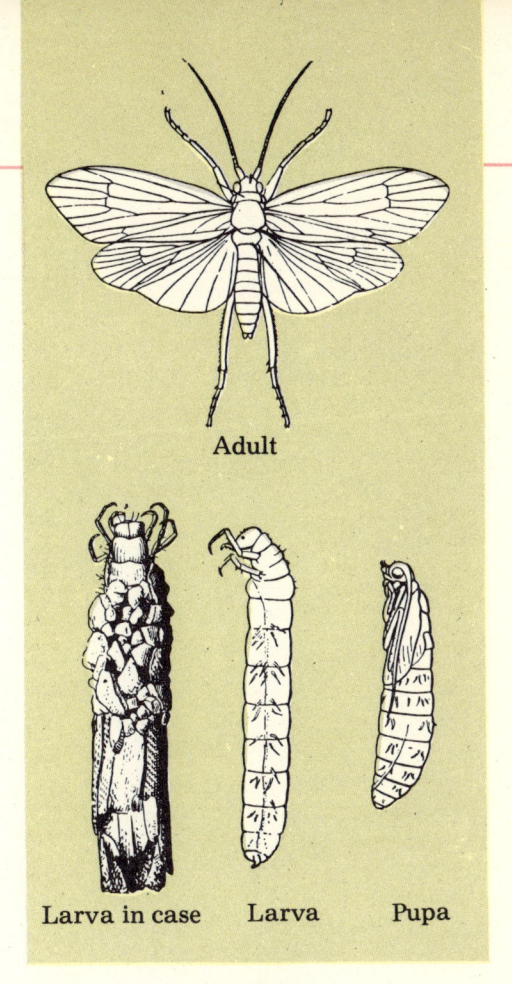

The larvae feed on small aquatic animals and plants. Some species make netlike structures that are fastened to the mouth of the case; these help anchor the case against the force of the current, and they may also help to trap food particles.

The larva pupates, or matures, inside the case. On developing into an adult, it must free itself from the case, swim to the surface of the pond, dry its newly formed wings, and begin a new existence as an air-breathing, flying insect.

—G.B.S.

Caddisfly

Adult

Larva in case   Larva   Pupa

CALIFORNIA; BIRDS OF
Some Birds of Central California

Californians are proud of their state. When they claim they have the biggest trees, the best of this, and the most of that, they are not stretching their imaginations. They are merely stating facts. There are many good reasons for being proud of the state they live in. The birdlife is impressive, and several species have ranges that do not extend far from the boundaries of the Golden State. In fact two, the yellow-billed magpie and the Santa Cruz jay, have never been found outside of California.

In central California it is possible in a few hours' drive to go from hot valleys and almost desert conditions to cool evergreen forests, and even snow fields on the tops of high mountains. In the country between San Francisco on the coast and Yosemite Park in the Sierras, there are many different habitats, each of which has a somewhat different birdlife.

1. Steller's jay. There are two types of blue jays in central California—one with a crest and one without. The crested or Steller's jays are birds of the pines and evergreens; the California jay prefers the oaks. Sometimes both may be seen in the same place, and they both rob the California woodpecker of its carefully laid stores of acorns. The loud **chack chack chack** of these jays is a familiar sound as they travel around in flocks amongst the pines. The nest is built in an evergreen, anywhere from 5 or 10 feet to 60 feet up. The eggs are greenish-blue with brownish spots. There are several slightly different races of the Steller's jay. The one that lives in the moist evergreen woods near the coast of central California is called the coast jay. The race in the Sierras is the blue-fronted jay.

2. California jay. The common blue jay of the oaks and scrub. Its **chack chack** notes are higher than those of the Steller's jay. California jays are year-round birds building their nests of twigs in bushes or low trees. The three to six spotted eggs are buffy-brown or greenish.

3. Bullock's oriole. Male. This, the only oriole in central California, can be told by its brilliant flame-orange breast and large white wing patches. The female is plainer, yellow below and olive above with two narrow white wing bars. Orioles are summertime birds, especially common about streams and on the trees about farms.

4. Brewer's blackbird. Male. The common blackbird. At close range males show purplish reflections on the head, greenish on the back. The eye is whitish. Females are gray-brown, but not streaked the way female redwings are. Males can be easily told from cowbirds, which have dark eyes, shorter bills and brown heads.

5. Allen's hummingbird. Male. The large Anna's hummer is an all-year-round bird, but the Allen's is more of a summer visitor, best identified by its rusty tail which it spreads as it hovers near a flower. Females do not have the red throat. The nest is a tiny cup plastered with lichens and mosses, saddled to some convenient support. The two tiny white eggs are about the size of beans.

6. Western kingbird. The kingbird, with its yellow breast, gray back, and black tail, is a typical flycatcher. It sits still on its perch at the tip of a tree or on a wire, spots a flying insect and dashes forth to snap it up. The common note is a wharp **whit**, but when the bird feels "talkative" it utters many shrill twittering notes. The three to five spotted eggs are laid in a nest of twigs and grass in trees or sometimes on buildings.

7. Western wood pewee. Like most other flycatchers the wood pewee sits still in an upright position on a branch waiting for a meal to fly by. There are several other small obscure-looking flycatchers with white wing bars, but they are all smaller than the pewee and have white eye-rings.

8. Say's phoebe. A flycatcher that resembles a robin in coloration—cinnamon breast and black tail. In the summer, it lives in canyons in dry country where it builds its nest on a ledge or rock, in the corner of a building or under a bridge. In migration and in winter, it is found more widely, but always in open country where it sits on weed stalks and fences.

9. California woodpecker. This clownish-looking bird of the oak trees is best known for its habit of stuffing acorns into small holes it drills for the purpose. Sometimes several woodpeckers will work on the trunk of one tree, till it is so studded with acorns that it looks as if it had some strange disease. Later the acorns are eaten at leisure. The jays make capital out of the woodpeckers' industry by helping themselves freely. The nest is like that of other woodpeckers—white eggs in a hole in a tree or pole.

10. Bewick's wren. This wren can be told from the house wren by the conspicuous white stripe over the eye and the white in the corners of the tail. Although in summer it likes the chaparral of the dry hillsides, it comes down in fall and winter to live around the houses and gardens. The song is similar to the song sparrow's The nest is built in a crevice or hole, sometimes in a bird box. Several races occur. The one from San Francisco Bay south along the

coast is called Vigors's wren. The one to the north of San Francisco Bay is the Nicasio wren. The bird of the Sacramento and San Joaquin valleys is the San Joaquin wren.

11. Wren-tit. The shy little wren-tit is heard often, but seldom seen. Its strange song, a series of notes all on the same pitch, like a little ball bouncing faster and faster, can be heard every month in the year from the dense chaparral on the dry hillsides. If one is lucky he will see a small dusky bird with cinnamon underparts and a long tail. Its cuplike nest in the low bushes holds three to five pale greenish-blue eggs.

12. Chestnut-backed chickadee. Chickadees can always be told by their caps and bibs. This species, with its rufous back and sides, is probably the handsomest of all its family. Among the tall evergreens along the coastal belt the chestnut-back leads the little bands of kinglets, creepers, and nuthatches in their search for tiny insects. Upside down and right-side up the little bird utters its cheerful husky **chick-a-dee-dee-dee-dee** notes. The nest of moss,

hairs, feathers, etc., is made in a hole in a stub.

13. Nuttall's sparrow. Several types of white-crowned sparrows are found in central California at different seasons of the year. Except for the white-crowns of the high sierras, this is the only breeding form. It lives close to the coast throughout the year, building its nest on the ground or in bushes. It can be told from the Gambel's sparrow, which comes down in the fall, by its yellower bill and darker coloration.

14. Fox sparrow. A large heavily streaked sparrow that rummages noisily among the dead leaves in brushy places. A dozen or more races of this bird come into central California in fall and winter; some are dark brown with a trace of rusty in the tail, others grayer with yellow bills. Not even experts can identify most of them in the field.

15. Golden-crowned sparrow. This good-looking sparrow associates with the Nuttall's and Gambel's sparrows in the winter but is shyer, not coming into the towns as often. It likes the tangled growths and brushy places where it stays till late April or early May before departing for its northern nesting grounds. Its song is three plaintive whistled notes going down the scale.

16. Hermit thrush. A dweller of the woodlands and shady places, distinguished as a thrush by its brown back and spotted breast; from other thrushes by its bright rusty tail. Its beautiful flutelike song is rarely heard except on its breeding grounds. Hermit thrushes are chiefly found in migration and in winter, but one race, the Monterey hermit thrush, breeds in cool, evergreen forests near the coast. The three or four blue-green eggs are laid in a nest in a low tree.

17. Russet-backed thrush. Told from the hermit thrush by the uniformly colored back and tail. Its song is flutelike but not so rich as that of the hermit thrush, with each phrase wheeling upward in pitch. It is the only thrush that sings in the low woodlands of California. The nest is built in a bush or small tree.

18. Western bluebird. Male. The blue and chestnut color identifies this bird from all others except the lazuli bunting which is lighter blue with white wing bars. It resides in the lower hills and the yellow pine belt of the mountains, coming down to the valleys in winter. It lays its pale bluish-green eggs in holes in trees or sometimes bird boxes.

Some Birds of Southern California

Probably no part of the United States has more different kinds of country, or habitats for birds, than southern California. There are high mountains crowned with cool pine forests, hot deserts, rocky hillsides, lush farmlands, willowy river-bottoms, broad marshes, sandy beaches and rocky shores. The highest spot and the lowest spot in the United States are here less than a hundred miles apart: Mt. Whitney, 14,501 feet high and Death Valley 310 feet below the level of the sea. The bird-life found between these two extremes is remarkable.

Many of the common birds of southern California have already been given special attention in the large series of Audubon bird leaflets. This special leaflet has been prepared to show a few of the more familiar birds which are not included in that series. The number beside each picture refers to the number accompanying the descriptions on these pages.

1. Nuttall's woodpecker. Male. If you see a small black and white woodpecker in the live oaks in the foothills or in a dry canyon it is probably this species. Sometimes it comes into the orchards and groves where the downy (or willow) woodpecker is often found, but the bars on the back identify it. Females do not have the red patch on the crown of the head. The nest and eggs are like those of other woodpeckers, 4 or 5 white eggs in a hole in a tree.

2. California thrasher. A large dull-brown bird, with a long curved bill. It likes brushy places, and valleys between the foothills. When it is disturbed it flies into a bush or runs along the ground with its tail held high. The song is musical, made up of short phrases; usually each phrase is repeated. It reminds one of the song of a mockingbird but is not quite so brilliant. The bulky nest is built in a bush. The eggs are greenish blue, with brown speckles. In the deserts in the southeastern part of the state two or three other thrashers are found that are difficult to tell apart.

3. Sage thrasher. In southern California the sage thrasher is probably best known in the winter. It is common in the deserts east of the mountains, and much less so west. Its size, streaked breast, white spots on the tail and mockingbird-like look identify it. It breeds in sage-covered plains from Ventura County, Cal., northward, placing its typical bulky thrasher nest of sticks in sage. The eggs are greenish blue speckled with brown. The song is a long warbled affair.

4. Arizona hooded oriole. (a — male; b — female.) This flame-colored beauty is a city bird that likes the palms lining the streets. There it builds its basketlike nest among the fronds. The male Bullock's oriole, which is just as brilliant, can

be told by its black crown. The hooded oriole has the top of the head orange. Female orioles are duller and quite difficult to tell apart. This species, which is only a summer visitor, does not sing much, its usual notes being a sharp **eek** or a chatter.

5. **Phainopepla.** The color plate shows the male, a slim glossy black bird with a slender crest. In flight a large white patch shows in each wing. The female is gray. Although the bird is most typical of the desert country, it is found in many other dry localities in southern California. It likes to eat mistletoe and pepper berries. The shallow nest is built straddling a convenient limb, and usually holds 2 or 3 speckled grayish or whitish eggs. In the nesting season the male sings a rather colorless song.

6. **Ash-throated flycatcher.** Flycatchers have a habit of quietly sitting upright, until they spot a passing insect, then they sally out and snap it up. This species is the only flycatcher in California with a rusty-red tail. The kingbirds, which are also flycatchers, have black

tails. It spends the summer in the low country and in dry canyons and foothills, where it nests in a hollow tree trunk or limb.

7. Cassin's kingbird. Kingbirds are really large flycatchers and feed on flying insects. The Cassin's kingbird and the somewhat commoner western kingbird, are almost alike, but the western is paler gray above, with narrow white sides on the tail. This species utters a low **cheer** or **chi bew** and sometimes a rapid **ki-doo, ki-doo, ki-doo**. Both kingbirds build open nests in trees or bushes. The western kingbird is chiefly a summer visitor, the Cassin's a year-round resident.

8. Western tanager. (a—male; b—female.) No other California bird has a bright red head and a yellow breast. The female can be told from the female orioles by her shorter stouter bill. Although the tanager is seen in many places in migration, it spends the summer in the mountains. Its song is made up of husky, musical phrases; its note is **pit-ic**.

9. Violet-green swallow. Both the tree swallow and the violet-green swallow are dark and glossy above, and clear white below. The best way to tell this species from the other is by the white patches at the base of the tail. Although it can be found nearly anywhere during migration it spends the summer in the yellow pine belt of the mountains, building its nest in some woodpecker hole, dark cavity or high crevice in the rocks. Swallows and swifts are among the fastest fliers, and the most tireless.

10. Black-chinned hummingbird. Male. Hummingbirds are the smallest of birds, no larger than hawk moths. Of the several kinds that occur in southern California this is one of the most familiar. In certain lights a band of bright blue-purple reflects from the black throat-patch. Females have white throats and are difficult to tell from other hummers. The tiny nest, which is usually built near water, holds 2 eggs the size of beans. Whirring past on transparent wings, or hanging in the air before a blossom, these tiny creatures hardly seem like birds.

11. Gambel's sparrow. In migration and in winter Gambel's sparrows are everywhere in the thickets and among the weeds. They sing their pleasant wheezy song all winter long. The Nuttall's sparrow looks very much like it but has yellow at the base of the bill and is darker.

12. Green-backed goldfinch. Male. A little bird with a yellow breast, black cap, and white patches in the wing. Females are paler and duller without the black cap. Like other goldfinches the song is canary-like and the flight characterized by swooping dips. Flocks of them feed among the weeds and utter a plaintive **tee-ee** when disturbed. The nest is small and cup-like, built in a small crotch of a bush or tree. The 4 or 5 eggs are pale bluish green.

13. Calaveras warbler. Among the other warblers in the spring and fall migrations this little bird is found. Its yellow throat, gray head and white eye-ring identify it. The Macgillivray's warbler has an eye-ring but the entire head is gray, throat included. In southern California, the Calaveras is a migrant, going further north in the mountains to breed.

14. Lutescent warbler. Olive-green above and dingy greenish-yellow below, with no wing-bars or other conspicuous marks. It is a migrant coming to California in March or April. The nest is built on the ground under a bush or tree and holds 3 to 5 speckled white eggs. The song is a weak trill dropping in pitch at the end. A darker type of this bird, called the dusky warbler, which lives chiefly on the Channel Islands, comes over to the mainland where it spends the winter.

15. Rock wren. Wrens are small energetic brown birds, most of them smaller than sparrows, with slender bills. Their tails are often cocked up over the back. This species lives on the boulder-strewn hillsides and on rocky slopes of mountains where it sings its lively chant. The nest is hidden among the rocks, and usually has a little pathway of pebbles and tiny pieces of stone leading up to the entrance. The 6 or 8 eggs are white with a few dark specks.

16. Canyon wren. In rocky canyons near little mountain streams the canyon wren pours out its song, a sweet series of clear curved notes tripping down the scale. Its dark chestnut belly and white throat identify it from other wrens. Often the canyon wren and the rock wren live together in the same cliff. The nest is built preferably near a stream, among the rocks and boulders or sometimes in the corner of a building.

17. Cactus wren. Much larger than any of the other wrens, all of eight inches long. The heavily spotted breast, white eye-stripe and white tips to the outer tail-feathers are all aids to identification. In the desert, and from San Diego north, locally in dry places to Los Angeles County, this bird builds its bulky nest of straw and sticks in thorny bushes or large cacti. It is shaped like a small football. The song is a strange, mechanical **chu-chu-chu-chu** less musical than most other wrens.

18. Western gnatcatcher. This little gray-and white bird, with its long black-and-white tail reminds one of a tiny mockingbird. It flits about the bushes and chaparral thickets, uttering a thin peevish *pee*. It has a song too, but so weak and squeaky that it usually passes unnoticed. The nest is a beautiful little firm-walled cup saddled to a branch or crotch of a bush or tree. The outside is plastered with tiny lichens from the trunks of trees. The small eggs are white spotted with rusty.

CANVASBACK (*See under Duck*)

Angel Arch is a spectacular attraction at Canyonlands National Park, Utah

CANYONLANDS NATIONAL PARK
Location—Southern Utah
Size—257,640 acres
Mammals—Mountain sheep, cougars, deer, antelope, coyotes, foxes, badgers, squirrels, skunks, kangaroo rats
Birdlife—Eagles, hawks, roadrunners, quail, songbirds
Plants—Desert vegetation on plains; some forests at high elevation

Canyonlands, in 1964 one of the newest and largest of the national parks in the United States, is a spectacularly eroded region of mountains, buttes, precipitous valleys, and burning desert. Its main value is scenic, for, though wildlife is present, the aridity of the region prevents a concentration such as is found in Yellowstone. Two deep canyons, those of the Green and the Upper Colorado Rivers, are within the boundaries of the park.

Accommodations—To be developed
Headquarters—To be selected

364 CAPE COD NATIONAL SEASHORE

Nauset Beach at Cape Cod National Seashore, Massachusetts

CAPE COD NATIONAL SEASHORE
Location—Eastern Massachusetts
Size—27,000 acres
Mammals—Muskrats, minks
Birdlife—Geese, ducks, gulls, terns, shorebirds, songbirds, depending upon the season
Plants—Dune vegetation, pinelands, hardwoods, white cedar swamp

Comprising most of the eastern shore of Cape Cod, the area includes parts of the towns of Orleans, Chatham, Eastham, Wellfleet, Truro, and Provincetown. This portion of the Cape is a terminal moraine, the southernmost boundary of a glacier. The bluffs along the ocean afford a superb view over the Atlantic.

Accommodations—In any of the Cape towns
Headquarters—Eastham

CAPITOL REEF NATIONAL MONUMENT
Location—South-central Utah
Size—51 square miles

The aridity of the region is responsible for a dearth of wildlife in this national monument, but it is also largely responsible for the splendid preservation of its geological features. Layers of colorful sandstone, deposited when the area was under water millions of years ago, have been eroded over the centuries. Wind-blown sand and the action of water have carved steep bluffs, towers, and battlements in many shades of white and red.

Accommodations—Capitol Reef Lodge, Fruita, Utah

Headquarters—In the monument; address: Torrey, Utah

CARACARA
Audubon's Caracara
Other Common Names—Mexican eagle, Mexican buzzard
Scientific Name—*Caracara cheriway auduboni*
Family—Falconidae (caracaras and falcons)
Order—Falconiformes
Size—Length, 22 inches
Range—South central Florida and southern Texas

Universally called Mexican eagle, or Mexican buzzard by the natives, the caracara derives its correct name from the fancied resemblance of its notes to the sounds, *ca-ra-ca-ra*. This has never seemed appropriate. The call is not often heard as the bird is usually silent; but it does become vocal when courting and the harsh, discordant cackle only faintly suggests the given name. However, birdcalls are notoriously difficult to render into words and what sounds like one thing to one person may sound different to another.

To watch a caracara give its cry is far more interesting than the sound produced. It appears to cost great effort and is accompanied by remarkable contortions. The head is raised and bent backward until the crown all but touches the upper part of the back, the notes proceeding in a jerky, convulsive manner. The whole aspect of the performance is strange and awkward.

Much of the caracara's time is spent on the ground, and a glance at the long, stout, and capable legs reveals this adaptation. It walks firmly and surely, with a considerable stride and a distinct air of stateliness and bearing. Although it alights freely enough in small trees and on fence posts, it is just as likely to be seen on the highway, or through the vegetation along the roadside.

This decided inclination for the ground does not appear to have impaired in the slightest its power to fly. Flight is strong and well sustained, the wings flapping rather rapidly, with alternate periods of sailing. It does not indulge in the common practice of soaring, as do many birds of prey; and when it does fly it is usually with the direct purpose of getting

Audubon's caracara

Audubon's caracaras, adults (foreground and in flight); immature (rear)

from one place to another without loss of time.

While in flight, the caracara is as unmistakable as when at rest. The white spots in the wings and the white area at the base of the tail are conspicuous and constitute good field marks. When the bird is at rest, the striking-looking head with its large, eaglelike beak, the orange skin about the base of the head, and the slightly crested crown all combine to render it a memorable sight.

In immature specimens the general body plumage is a rusty-brown with the light areas not well defined, the whole effect being somewhat ragged. The old adult is different; the body is almost black, and the white patches the more conspicuous by contrast. In such plumage, the fine, wavy barring of the back of the neck is noticeable and attractive, and the entire aspect of the bird is strikingly handsome.

In its nesting habits, the caracara exhibits a tendency to select a single species of tree in which to build. This is the cabbage palm, or palmetto, which is so abundant on the Kissimmee Prairie of Florida. So marked is its nesting preference for this tree that nests found anywhere else are unusual. Choosing, as a rule, a small "hammock" of these trees, it builds its nest among the bases of the fronds, close to the trunk. So inconspicuous is it that one can stand directly beneath the tree and see little of the structure (*See also Bird: Nests and Nesting*).

The nest is rather bulky and well made of sticks, and lined with smaller twigs and sometimes shreds of moss. The eggs are two or three and show tremendous variations in shades, but are usually heavily marked with brown or chocolate, on a lighter background. Occasionally some eggs are sparsely marked, and now and then an almost immaculate one is found in a nest containing others of normal color. The youngsters are no less attractive than the eggs, soon becoming covered with a light-colored down, this giving place to the brownish immature plumage.

The caracara takes both living prey and carrion, thus exhibiting traits of both hawk and vulture. Lizards, snakes, turtles, and turtles' eggs are favorite food items. The bird is often seen on the shoulders of roads or ditch banks, digging open a turtle nest in the loose soil. It must watch at times for the turtle to lay, standing by as it scrapes out the hollow for its eggs. A yellow-bellied turtle was once found laying its eggs on the bank of a drainage canal, the process at the time being almost complete. About twenty minutes later a caracara was seen digging out the nest and eating the eggs, all but two or three of which had already been devoured. The bird must have watched from nearby as the turtle laid its eggs and then covered them (*See under Reptile; also under Turtle*).

The caracara shares with the turkey and black vultures the role of scavenger. Apparently there is little antagonism between it and the vultures; what there is, is intermittent and variable. The caracara has been seen eating a dead animal while vultures sat about in a circle at some distance. At other times, both have been seen to feed together in perfect amity.

The settling of open country has taken its toll of the caracara population. In any cattle state, however, such as Florida or Texas, wide ranges will no doubt exist for years to come, thus assuring the continuance of the typical habitat of the species. In the Kissimmee Prairie area, this species is a special charge of the National Audubon Society wardens, and protection has been afforded it ever since such guardianship was instituted in that region in 1936. The results have been gratifying. The caracara is not abundant, but it is seen throughout the entire year. Continued protection and no change in the character of the country itself will assure its future. Its status on the coastal plain of Texas may not be quite so satisfactory, but it persists in suitable locali-

368 CARDINAL

ties, and enough open range remains there to assure long residence for some pairs. —A.S., Jr.

CARDINAL
Other Common Names—Redbird, Virginia nightingale
Scientific Name— *Richmondena cardinalis*
Family—Fringillidae (grosbeaks, finches, sparrows, and buntings)
Order—Passeriformes
Size—Length, eight to nine inches
Range—Nests east of the Great Plains and in southern California, Arizona, New Mexico, and Texas. Winters in same areas since it is nonmigratory

The cardinal, the state bird of Illinois, Indiana, Kentucky, North Carolina, Ohio, Virginia, and West Virginia, lives along woodland borders, along roadsides, swamps, and suburban yards in the eastern United States. It is doubtful whether these birds travel more than two or three miles from their birthplace during their lifetime. Of course, if a neighborhood has too many cardinals, there is a tendency for the young to wander into a new territory where things are not so crowded. That is what seems to have happened in some parts of the northern states during recent years. The cardinal has established itself in parts of Minnesota, Michigan, New York, and even southern Ontario, where it was not found formerly; in fact, the bird is now one of the three or four most common birds in Cleveland, Ohio, where it was said to have been scarce a half-century ago. The cardinal, then, in spite of its brilliant color, is a bird that has successfully adapted itself to civilization. There seems little doubt that there are more cardinals living today than in the past.

The male cardinal is a bright red bird with a little black about the bill, and

The cardinal has a wide range in the eastern United States and the Southwest

with a crest. It is often said that beautiful birds are poor singers but this is not true of the cardinal. The songs in its repertoire are more like chants, however, a series of clear, rapid whistles sounding like *whoit-whoit-whoit*, or *kew-kew-kew-kew*, or *what-cheer what-cheer what-cheer*. Perched at the tip of some shrub or sapling, the male pours forth a cascade of notes—especially in the early morning when the world is waking. Cardinals sing at almost any time during the year—even when nesting time is months away. Even the females sing a soft, subdued song.

The cardinal builds an open nest among dense shrubbery. Hedges and tangles of briars are favorite spots. A cardinal likes an informal, wild garden much better than one that is well groomed, where the tangles have been cut away.

The bulky nest is built of shreds of bark, weed stems, and dead leaves. It is cupped quite deeply and lined with fine stems and rootlets. Although it is usually built not more than three or four feet from the ground, it is occasionally placed as high as 30 feet in a vine-covered sapling.

The three or four eggs are white and spotted or dotted with dull brown. Often one egg is very different from the others—much smaller and whiter, almost as if it were laid by some other bird. The fledged young ones are yellow-brown, resembling the female parent. Two, and sometimes three, broods are raised in a season.

When leaves drop from the trees and the days become cooler, two and three families of cardinals often gather together into a small flock. Some come to feeding trays that people have placed outside their windows or in their yards. They seem to like sunflower seeds best of all the foods that are put out for them, although they will also consume nutmeats and corn. Their stout bills are well adapted for cracking seeds. —A.B., Jr.

Cardinal flower

CARDINAL FLOWER
Other Common Names—Red lobelia, red betty
Scientific Name—*Lobelia cardinalis*
Family—Campanulaceae (bluebell family)
Range—New Brunswick to Florida; west to Colorado
Habitat—Shaded streams and moist fields
Time of Blooming—July through September

The cardinal flower is one of the most intensely colored among native American wildflowers. The tall, rigidly erect plant is a perennial. Its numerous leaves are thin and oblong, and pointed at both ends. The leafy stalk produces a loose cluster of 15 to 20 flowers at the top of the spike. The blossoms grow from an inch to one and one-half inches long and bloom from the bottom of the spike upward.

The cardinal flower is an example of the bright color often highly developed in plants that are pollinated by birds or insects. Because of the flower's vivid red coloring, the tiny hummingbird is a frequent visitor to it, and these birds gather in large numbers where it is plentiful. Hummingbirds are able to reach into the flower with their long tongues and sip the nectar that is inaccessible to most insects. Thus, they are the chief pollinators of this plant.

Besides producing seeds, the cardinal flower forms new plants by sending out offshoots from the top of the root. Because it has been overpicked by people who admire its lovely flowers, it has been entirely exterminated in many places where it once grew abundantly.

Throughout the eastern United States and as far west as Colorado it grows in the moist soil of meadows and marshes, wet ravines, swamps, stream banks, and ditches.

The cardinal flower is a member of the family, *Campanulaceae* consisting of about 20 genera and 600 species. Many members of the family contain a narcotic poison in their milky sap. *Lobelia inflata*, called Indian tobacco, is an example. —A.M.M.

CARIBOU

The caribou is well adapted for its life in the forests and frigid, barren grounds of the North. The winter pelage consists of long, hollow, air-filled guardhairs, below which is a thick, woolly undercoating. This coat conserves the warmth of the body and affords an adequate protection against the icy storms and frigid winds of the animal's habitat. Even the nose is hair-covered. The hoofs are broad and spreading and thus are suitable for traveling over soft muskeg or winter snow. To obtain its winter food of moss and lichens, the caribou must dig down through the snow, and the broad hoofs make efficient snow shovels.

The Old World reindeer and the North American caribou are so closely related that they are now considered as one species, *Rangifer tarandus*. Caribou and reindeer does are the only female deer with antlers.

Caribou are divided into three groups according to their habitat, and the differences in environment have slightly modified the appearance and habits of the various subspecies.

Barren Ground Caribou
Other Common Names—Caribou, reindeer
Scientific Name—*Rangifer tarandus arcticus*
Family—Cervidae (deer)
Order—Artiodactyla
Size—Male: body length, 5¼ to 6½ feet; height at shoulder, 3¼ to 3½ feet; weight, 150 to 450 pounds. Females smaller
Range—Arctic tundra in summer; partially open spruce forests in winter

The barren ground caribou has an extensive range. These caribou live throughout most of northern North America, including the arctic islands and Greenland, south to the ranges of the woodland caribou. In general, they differ from the woodland caribou in their shorter legs and in the shape of their antlers. The main beam of the antlers of the barren ground caribou is more cylindrical in shape. Its antlers are much longer, too, with a backward and then forward curve; the branching and palmation are at the extremity. However, this is not always the case, for both types of horns and intermediates may be found among a single herd.

The barren ground caribou migrates southward in winter in search of food

Nine subspecies are recognized. The typical barren ground caribou, *Rangifer tarandus arcticus,* inhabits the barren grounds from the Mackenzie River east to Hudson Bay. Cabot's caribou, *Rangifer tarandus caboti,* of northern Quebec and Labrador is noted for the length of its antlers. One of these caribou holds the world's record with a length of 74-1/2 inches. Two subspecies have been described from the coasts of Greenland —*Rangifer tarandus eogroenlandicus,* of the northeastern coast and *Rangifer tarandus groenlandicus* of the southwestern coast. The former is now believed to be extinct. On Ellesmere Island and other of the neighboring arctic islands the nearly white Peary's caribou, *Rangifer tarandus pearyi,* occurs. This is the smallest of the caribou. Stone's caribou, *Rangifer tarandus stonei,* inhabits most of Alaska and western Yukon; Grant's caribou, *Rangifer tarandus granti,* is restricted to the Alaskan Peninsula and Unimak Island. The mountains of southern Yukon and northern British Columbia are the habitat of Osborne's caribou, *Rangifer tarandus osborni.* Unlike many of the barren ground group this form does not migrate to any extent. The least known of the caribou is the small Queen Charlotte Islands' caribou,

Rangifer tarandus dawsoni. Although at one time thought to be extinct, evidence now shows that it may still exist in small numbers in the mountainous parts of these islands.

The third type, the mountain caribou, is a very large, dark animal with antlers quite similar to those of the barren ground caribou. This deer is found in the mountains of southern British Columbia and Alberta. It ranged in former years as far south as Washington and Idaho. Two forms are recognized—the mountain caribou, *Rangifer tarandus montanus,* of British Columbia and *Rangifer tarandus fortidens* of Alberta. In the eastern foothills of Alberta; this caribou appears to merge with the woodland caribou.

The barren ground caribou is noted for its migrations. Undoubtedly the main reason for these movements is the quest for food. In summer, when food is plentiful, the animals not only feed on lichens but browse on willows and other leaves and twigs. They also spend much time grazing on the rich grasses on the mountain slopes and highland meadows; caribou in reality are mountain animals and, when possible, spend much of the summer in the higher altitudes. When winter comes and vegetation is no longer available, the caribou must search for winter food. This consists chiefly of lichens, mosses, and dried grasses, which must be found where the snow is not too deep. Some of these migrations may be but a few miles while others take the animal great distances. These migrations are not always over the same route each year, and many Indians and Eskimos have starved when the caribou have not arrived as expected.

The Indians and Eskimos of certain regions of Alaska and northern Yukon are so dependent on the caribou for food and clothing that where the great herds decreased in size domesticated reindeer were introduced to replenish the food supply. These reindeer have become well established, much to the detriment of the remaining native caribou, which have to compete with them for their natural food. Some of the reindeer have joined the caribou herds and hybridization has taken place.

—T.D.C.

Eastern Woodland Caribou
Other Common Names—Caribou, reindeer
Scientific Name—*Rangifer tarandus caribou*
Family—Cervidae (deer)
Order—Artiodactyla
Size—Male: body length, 5½ to 8 feet; height at shoulder, 3½ to 4 feet; weight, 150 to 700 pounds. Females smaller
Range—Subarctic coniferous forests of Canada

The woodland caribou is found in the forested areas of southern Canada from Newfoundland to Alberta and north as far as Labrador, St. James Bay, and the District of Mackenzie. This caribou is characterized by the shorter, more flattened beam and broad palmation of the antlers, giving the animal a somewhat compact appearance. There are three subspecies of this caribou: the Newfoundland caribou, *Rangifer tarandus terraenovae;* the eastern woodland caribou, *Rangifer tarandus caribou;* and the slightly darker western woodland caribou, *Rangifer tarandus sylvestris.* The Newfoundland caribou is restricted to that island. The eastern form merges with the western in western Ontario. The eastern woodland caribou is now becoming rare or has disappeared from much of its former range. It was once found in the forests of the northern New England states. At the present time it is believed that the only native caribou found south of the St. Lawrence River is a small herd inhabiting the mountains of the interior of the Gaspe Peninsula. Very recently caribou from Newfoundland were introduced on Mt. Katahdin, Maine. —T.D.C.

The eastern woodland caribou lives in the spruce-fir forests of Canada

374 CARLSBAD CAVERNS

Stalactites and stalagmites fill weird chambers in Carlsbad Caverns, New Mexico

CARLSBAD CAVERNS NATIONAL PARK
Location—Southeastern New Mexico
Size—45,526 acres
Mammals—Cougars, gray foxes, coyotes, bobcats, mule deer
Birdlife—Roadrunners, Inca doves, cactus wrens, painted redstarts
Plants—Ocotillos, chollas, cacti

This park is mostly underground and draws many visitors to its cavern marvels. These are made up of a series of connected rooms, the largest of which is some 1,300 feet long and 650 feet wide and rises 200 feet above the path (*See also under Cave Life*). Park department guides lead parties as large as several hundred people through the caverns, which have been altered by man to include electric lights and elevators
Accommodations—None available at the park
Headquarters—Carlsbad Caverns National Park, New Mexico

CARNIVORE

The carnivores are medium to large terrestrial mammals of the order Carnivora. Examples are wolves, the coyote, foxes, bears, raccoons, weasels, skunks, hyaenas, the cougar, lynx, and otters. The most important feature distinguishing them from other mammals is their diet, which is predominantly meat; the high development of their shearing teeth (called carnassials, or dog-teeth); the simple one-compartmented stomach; the short length of their intestines; the presence usually of five toes (or at least four), all of which have claws; and the large, well-developed brain. —J.K.T.

Recommended Reading
Introduction to Mammalogy—E. Lendell Cockrum. The Ronald Press, New York.

The black bear is a member of the order Carnivora

CARP
Eruopean Carp
Other Common Names—German carp
Scientific Name—*Cyprinous carpio*
Family—Cyprinidae (minnows and carps)
Order—Cypriniformes
Size—Length, 12 to 30 inches; weight, up to 20 or 25 pounds
Range—Artificially introduced from its native continent, Asia, to many European countries and throughout the United States. In waters of the United States they are most abundant in the central and midwestern states

The body is fairly stout. The mouth is toothless, but teeth are present in the throat. The upper jaw has two short fleshy barbels on each side. The front barbels are considerably shorter than the rear barbels. The dorsal fin (*See under Fish: Topography of a Fish*) is long and its first ray is a spine that is serrated at its rear. This spinous ray is followed by 16 or more soft rays. The fin slopes gradually downward toward the rear of the fish. The anal fin is shorter than the dorsal fin but also has a serrated, spinous front ray. This ray is followed by five or six soft rays.

Asiatic carps are divided into three varieties, depending upon the presence or absence of scales; the scale carps are fully scaled; the mirror carps have only a few scales which are very large; the leather carps have no scales at all.

The carp's back is slaty-olive or golden-olive in color. Its upper sides are lighter and have a bronze cast; the lower sides are golden-yellow to silvery. The scales of the yellowish-white belly have a dark spot at the base, and are dark-edged, giving the fully scaled variety of carp a cross-hatched appearance. The dorsal fin and tail fin are gold-green. The other fins are yellow.

Carps are voracious feeders. They eat both animal and vegetable matter. Although they are considered fine food in Europe and Asia, they are not eaten as extensively in North America. This, coupled with the facts that they compete with more popular game fish and sometimes muddy the water with their bottom activities, has made them unpopular. As a result there have been extensive efforts to eliminate them from waters in which they are numerous.
—M.R.

Wild carrot

CARROT
Wild Carrot
Other Common Name—Bird's nest, Queen Anne's lace
Scientific Name—*Daucus carota*
Family—Umbelliferae (parsley family)
Range—Throughout cultivated areas of North America
Habitat—Roadsides, waste places, and old fields
Time of Blooming—June to first frost

The tiny white flowers are five-petaled and differ in size. There are small ones within larger ones. The flowers grow in clusters at the end of a long stiff stalk that gives each stalk the appearance of an opened umbrella. These stalks are numerous, sometimes as many as twenty-five growing together from the end of a branch. In the center of this floral umbrella there is a tiny red spot isolated on its own stalk. The purpose of this floret has not been determined.

Since the nectar of this flower is secreted in an open disk, it is accessible to the shortest-tongued of insects. The flower is pollinated chiefly by flies, bees, and wasps (*See Pollination*), although more than 60 species of insects visit the wild carrot, none of which seem to object to its strong pungent odor.

The wild carrot was cultivated in Europe and Asia for more than 1,000 years. Although now considered a pernicious weed, this plant is a member of the parsley family—to which carrots belong—and it is believed to be the stock from which the present-day garden carrot developed. It grows in waste places, old fields, and along roadsides in most parts of the country.

The wild carrot is more commonly called Queen Anne's lace in some regions because of its delicate lacelike appearance. —A.M.M.

CASHEW (*See under Sumac*)

CATS OF NORTH AMERICA
Cats are carnivorous mammals belonging to the family Felidae, a group that is widely distributed over the tropical, temperate, and subarctic regions of all the continents except Australia. Cats live also on many islands which in late geological periods have had connections with continental masses. There are various genera and many species belonging to this family, ranging in size from the great tiger of India and Siberia to the common house cat.

No matter where they live, or to what sizes they develop, cats are cats. They are intelligent and highly specialized carnivores, and except for the differences in size and the pelage colors and patterns which distinguish the various species from each other, these animals adhere to a rather uniform structural design. They are all active, lithe hunters. Most of them are tree climbers, and they are all surefooted, wherever they may be. All but one form, the cheetah of Africa and Asia, have retractile claws with which they may grasp their prey or tear their adversaries. They are all

The cougar, or mountain lion, is the largest cat in the United States

highly specialized in the skull. The face is short and the teeth are limited in function to the slashing of the powerful canines and the scissorlike cutting of the highly evolved carnassials—the two cheek teeth on either side of the head that serve to chop meat into ingestible chunks. Some cats, those of the lynx group, have short tails and rather long legs, but these are structural differences of relatively minor importance.

The cats of North America may be divided into two general groups, namely the long-tailed cats and the short-tailed lynxes. In the long-tailed group are the jaguar, the mountain lion or cougar, the ocelot, and the jaguarundi, eyra, or "otter cat" as it is called in southwestern Mexico. In the short-tailed group are the large Canada lynx and the bobcat, commonly known as the wildcat.

The jaguar is a cat of the tropics and the warmer portions of North America. It ranges through considerable areas in South America, comes up through the isthmus into Mexico, where it is fairly common, and extends into the southernmost limits of Arizona, New Mexico and Texas. In the southwestern United States this big cat, the largest of the North American felines, is rare at present, but it would seem probable that before the days of the white man the jaguar was fairly common in the area immediately to the north of the Rio Grande river.

The jaguar is a large, heavy cat; the stocky build is very characteristic. The head is broad and rounded. The pelage has a tawny yellow ground color, with large blackish rosettes covering the entire body. The jaguar may be distinguished from the Old World leopard by its heavier build and by the rosettes on its coat of fur, compared with the spots of the leopard.

The cougar, variously known as the mountain lion, puma, catamount, painter, and panther, is one of the very characteristic North American cats, and it holds a prominent place in the history, both actual and legendary, of the settlement of the United States. It is a large yellowish-brown cat of rather slender build, with a rounded head and a long, heavy tail. Among modern mammals, the mountain lion is remarkable for its wide distribution; indeed, few animals other than man have surpassed this large cat in the extent of their range or the variety of their environments. Prior to the coming of the white man the cougar ranged from Canada throughout temperate North America, through the isthmus and over much of the continent of South America to the southernmost extremity of Patagonia. At one time the cougar had been exterminated in the eastern and central portions of North America, with the exception of Florida, but is reappearing in the East where large populations of deer occur. This cat is an active predator, living to a large degree upon deer (See Cougar, and under Deer).

The ocelot and the jaguarundi, although technically known as North American cats, are, like the jaguar, more properly tropical and hot climate animals. Therefore one finds them in the North American region mainly in Mexico, with very slight extensions into Texas.

The ocelot, also called tiger cat and leopard cat, is perhaps one of the most beautiful cats in the world. It is a small member of the cat family, a hunter of small game, and an animal usually about twice the size of an ordinary house cat. It is beautifully marked by spots, many of which are elongated to produce a flowing design. The colors are various but center around dark yellows, browns, and black.

Of all the American cats, the jaguarundi is probably the least known. This small cat is comparable to the ocelot in size and in habits, although it does not hesitate to take to water—a rather unusual trait among the cats. It is a long, low cat, with comparatively short legs. There are two color phases, one gray and one red.

The short-tailed cats, the northern lynx and the bobcat, are typically North

Because of overhunting, the bobcat is now rare in many areas

American and like the cougar, they figure largely in the actual and legendary history of the continent. The Canada lynx is a medium-sized carnivore, weighing about 30 pounds. It is long-legged, with large feet that in winter help to keep it from sinking into the deep snow. The fur is a light gray in winter and brown in summer; it has long tufts of hair on its ears. It is a hunter of small game, particularly the snowshoe rabbit.

The more southern relative of the Canada lynx is the bobcat, a characteristic cat of the United States. It is somewhat smaller than the lynx, and the ground color of the fur is a deep reddish brown, overlain by brown or black spots.

Cats as such made their appearance at the beginning of the Oligocene period, some 40 million years ago (*See Geological time*). They evolved from certain primitive carnivorous mammals known as miacids, as did all other modern land-living carnivores.

A remarkable fact about the cats is that from their beginnings in Oligocene times they were highly specialized, different only in some minor details from the cats of today. It would seem that there was a sudden rush of evolutionary development whereby the cats became established and thoroughly specialized at the beginning of their long history. In other words, it is a highly developed type of animal, fixed as to its modifications and habits, which appeared in Oligocene times and has persisted until the present day. This is the key to the general structural uniformity of the cats.

Cats are all alike, except for the minor

points of size and coloration. Because they are evolutionarily rigid — they show little of the structural plasticity that characterizes, for instance, the dog family. And this is a key also to the fact that cats may be tamed but never truly domesticated. The common house cat is basically a small tiger which will revert easily to a wild one. It is a thoroughly independent animal, not at all like the dog which becomes dependent upon its human master.

From the beginnings of their history, cats followed two general lines of development. One of these lines was that of the feline cats, the long-tailed cats and the lynxes of the modern world. The other was the line of machaerodont, or saber-toothed cats, a group which is now extinct. The saber-toothed cats developed side by side with the feline cats, and had a highly successful evolutionary history, for the last of these animals disappeared only a few thousand years ago.

Saber-toothed tigers were heavy, powerful cats, in which the upper canine teeth were enormously enlarged to form huge sabers that projected down below the border of the lower jaw, even when the mouth was closed. Of all the Felidae the saber-toothed cats were the most highly specialized, not only as to the development of the powerful, stabbing weapons, but also in the structure of the skull, of the carnassials, or meat-cutting teeth, and in certain characters of the body. Perhaps it was this specialization that spelled their doom, for when the large animals on which they preyed became extinct at the end of the ice age, or Pleistocene period, the saber-toothed cats became extinct, too. They were unable to compete with their more active, though less powerful, feline cousins in the pursuit of fast-running animals.

It is to be hoped that the modern native cats of North America will enjoy a long history — a hope about which one's feelings cannot be too sanguine. At the present time, and for years past, there has been much sentiment in favor of exterminating the cougar, and to a lesser extent the lynx, because these cats are predators that occasionally make raids upon livestock and poultry.

However, studies in recent years show that these cats play a useful role in the workings of nature. The deer, and likewise the rabbits, if uncontrolled, multiply excessively and do much damage to the forest cover. Man can control these animals after a fashion, but efficient control depends largely upon natural agents. And among these natural agents are the predatory cats, the mountain lions, and the lynxes (See under *Balance of Nature; Biological Control*).

Moreover, what would it be like if the camper in the Rockies or the Sierras could go to sleep at night without the thrill of knowing that he was being watched from the shadows by the great, wild eyes of the cougar and the lynx?
— E.H.C.

Jaguar

Recommended Reading

Field Book of North American Mammals — H. E. Anthony. Putnam's, New York.
King of Cats and his Court — Victor H. Cahalane. *National Geographic Magazine*, February 1943.
Lives of North American Game Animals — Ernest Thompson Seton. Doubleday, Doran, New York.
The World of the Bobcat — Joe Van Wormer. J. B. Lippincott Company, Philadelphia.

CATALPA
Southern Catalpa

Other Common Names — Eastern catalpa, Indian bean, bean tree, Indian cigar tree, cigar tree, catawba tree

Scientific Name — *Catalpa bignonoides*

Family — Martyniaceae (martynia family)

Range — Originally found in southern United States. Now widely used as an ornamental plant in all states east of Rocky Mountains and north to New England

Habitat — The native southern catalpa grows in moist, fertile soil along the southern coast. This hardy tree has been widely planted and endures shade and dry soil conditions well. The western species, *Catalpa speciosa*, is more resistant to frost

Leaves — Large, simple leaves 6 to 10 inches long and 4 to 5 inches wide. Underside, downy. Late in appearing. Turn brown and drop in early fall

Bark — Silvery gray, deeply furrowed; thick and scaly

Flowers — White flowers with purple and gold spots on petals; bloom in June or July in upright clusters covering the tree; heavy fragrance

Fruit — Elongated, cigar-shaped capsule containing many winged seeds; may persist on the tree throughout winter

The catalpa is the only member of its large tropical family, the Bignoniaceae, that grows to tree size north of the subtropics. The family is noted for its showy, trumpet-shaped, irregular flowers. The catalpa's large panicles of purple-etched white blossoms, and the large, light green leaves make it a showy ornamental and shade tree. The long, cigarlike seed pods help make it one of the easiest trees to recognize.

There are two species of native catalpa in the United States. Both have been so widely and successfully planted as shade trees that we are today unsure of their original distribution.

The southern catalpa, *Catalpa bignonoides,* was apparently originally restricted to the extreme southeast, occurring from Georgia and northern Florida to Tennessee. It is often tall, 25 to 40 feet and sometimes as much as 60, and has a slender crown. The best identifying mark, aside from the bark of mature trees, is the dense, many-flowered blossom. Being more "southern" in nature, it flowers later than the northern catalpa where both occur together out of the original range.

The other common species is *Catalpa speciosa*, the northern or western catalpa. Its large leaves taper to a long point and the flower clusters are open and few-flowered. The bark is thin and scaly. This species has always had a more extensive range, growing as a native tree from Arkansas to Tennessee, north to Illinois and Indiana.

To make identification more difficult, however, two species from China have also been planted, mostly in the western United States. —R.C.C.

Catalpa tree seed pods

The catbird is an expert mimic and often immitates other birds or even frogs

CATBIRD
Other Common Names — Black-capped thrush, chicken bird, slate-colored mockingbird, cat flycatcher
Scientific Name — *Dumetella carolinensis*
Family — Mimidae (mockingbirds and thrashers)

Order — Passeriformes
Size — Length, 8½ to 9¼ inches
Range — Nests from central British Columbia, central Saskatchewan, southern Ontario, southern Quebec, and Nova Scotia, south to western Washington, northeastern Oregon, northern Utah,

it is actually quite harmless. The brownish or greenish material that most caterpillars regurgitate when disturbed is merely partly digested food and only rarely has an objectionable odor.

Food

Though nearly all caterpillars eat plants (one exception, the larva of the harvester butterfly, *Feniseca tarquinis*, feeds on plant lice), they feed in different ways. Most of the larger caterpillars eat the edges of leaves. Some of the smaller caterpillars skeletonize a leaf by eating only between the veins or ribs of the leaf. Other caterpillars eat holes in leaves. The leaf miners feed entirely within the leaf, and from a linear, trumpet-shaped, or blotchlike cavity inside it. A few caterpillars live in galls (*See under Gall and under Insect*). The spindle-shaped gall on the stems of goldenrod constitutes the home and food of the larva of the goldenrod gall moth. A few others, such as the larva of the carpenter moth, bore into wood.

Silk

Caterpillars have well-developed silk glands, which are modified salivary glands that open on their lower lip. Many (but not all) caterpillars use their silk in making a cocoon. Although a number of the large moths make an elaborate silken cocoon, the silkworm moth, *Bombyx mori*, is the only one whose silk is of commercial value. Some of the very hairy caterpillars, such as the wooly bears, use very little silk in making their cocoons. They make them largely out of their own body hairs.

One of the most interesting uses of caterpillar silk is in the making of shelters. Some caterpillars roll up a leaf, tie it in place with a thread of silk, and feed inside the shelter thus formed. Many butterfly larvae construct leaf shelters but use them only as a retreat or as a shelter in which to spend the winter. Some caterpillars tie a number of leaves together and make a "tent." A single tent is usually constructed by an entire family of caterpillars, which may feed entirely within the tent, or feed outside it and use it only as a retreat.

The tent caterpillar, *Malacosoma americana*, and the webworms are well known tent makers. These silken tents may be unsightly objects on trees or shrubbery, but they shelter an interesting family of caterpillars. The tent-making caterpillars usually leave the tent permanently when they are ready to pupate.

A few caterpillars use their silk to tie together little parts of leaves or twigs in order to make a case or bag within which they live. If they move about, they do so without coming completely out of the case. When they are ready to transform, or pupate, they do so inside the case.

The bagworm, which is often common on evergreen shrubbery, is a good example of a case-making caterpillar. Many caterpillars when falling from a leaf spin a thread of silk which serves to lower them safely to the ground.

Pupae

When a caterpillar becomes full grown it transforms into a pupa for a resting stage that precedes its transformation into an adult winged insect. Some caterpillars spin elaborate cocoons and transform inside the cocoon; others make only a simple cocoon; still others make no cocoon at all, and pupate in some protected place or attach themselves to a leaf or twig. Many moths pupate under the ground; on the surface among the leaves; or under a log or stone. A pupa is an elongated, mummylike object. In the pupae of butterflies and moths the appendages of the adult insect can be seen folded down under the pupal skin. Moth pupae are usually dark brown; butterfly pupae may be variously colored. The pupa, or chrysalis, of the monarch butterfly (*See under Butterfly*) is light green, ornamented with yellow spots

The caterpillar of the polyphemus moth

("the green box with the golden nails").

The pupae of most butterflies are called *chrysalises*. A chrysalis may be attached to and suspended from a leaf or twig by the transforming caterpillar's tail, or be attached by the tail and held in a more or less upright position against the leaf or twig by a silken girdle about the middle of the pupa's body. The pupae of the monarch, fritillaries, anglewings, mourning cloak, admirals, purples, viceroy, wood nymphs, and other butterflies hang by the tail. The pupae of the blues, coppers, hairstreaks, whites, sulfurs, and swallowtails are held upright by a silken girdle.

Caterpillars as Food

Birds, predacious insects such as ground beetles, and many other animals feed on caterpillars, and a number of flies and wasps parasitize them. Insects that parasitize caterpillars usually lay their eggs on or in the body of the caterpillar. Upon hatching, the larvae of the parasite begin to feed on the inner tissues of the caterpillar. Sometimes the caterpillar pupates before it is killed by the parasite, and the parasite (or parasites—often a good many live in a single caterpillar) emerges from the pupa instead of the butterfly or moth. In other cases the caterpillar is killed before it can pupate. The proportion of caterpillars that become parasitized is sometimes very high, as those who try to rear them in captivity discover.

Keeping Caterpillars in Captivity

Most of the feeding and developmental stages of caterpillars can be seen by anyone who takes the trouble to observe them. They can be watched among their natural surroundings, or they can be caged and kept indoors. In the field they can often be confined to their food plant by a screen or cloth wrapped around the plant or branch on which they are feeding. Many people who cage caterpillars are interested only in their transformations; their other habits are often just as interesting, however. If a caterpillar is found feeding, additional food of this same type should be given it after it is caged. If it is found wandering about and not feeding, and its food plant is not known, it may be nearly ready to pupate or hibernate and need not be provided with food after being caged.

Most caterpillars can be kept indoors very easily. All that is necessary usually is to provide food and a ventilated container. The food should be fresh. New leaves should be provided every day or so, or the twigs bearing the leaves may be placed in a jar of water; or the plant on which the caterpillars feed can be grown in the cage (if it is not too big). Almost anything will serve as a cage— a glass jar with a wire screen or cloth over the top, a lamp chimney or celluloid cylinder over a potted plant, a cardboard box with cellophane windows, a glass box (an aquarium, or glass plates fastened together with adhesive tape) covered with a screen, or a wooden framework covered with screening.

It is often desirable to have some loose soil, sand, or leaves in the bottom of the cage, particularly if the caterpillar is one that pupates in the ground. If cages containing pupae are kept indoors during the winter, the adults will usually emerge a month or two sooner than they normally do. Oftentimes, however, the rearing will be more successful if the cages are kept out of doors. Overwintering larvae kept indoors are likely to become active before their food plant is available outdoors.

There is no simple way to identify the many kinds of caterpillars. The references listed below describe or illustrate some of the more common kinds. Different caterpillars vary greatly in their food habits and life cycle; some overwinter in the pupal stage and emerge as adults the following year, others overwinter as caterpillars, and still others pass the winter in the egg stage. The accompanying table gives some information on the food plants and overwintering stages of a few of the more common caterpillars. —D.J.B.

Recommended Reading

The Butterfly Book—W. J. Holland, Doubleday & Company, Garden City, New York.
Field Book of Insects—Frank E. Lutz. G. P. Putnam's Sons, New York.
A Field Guide to the Butterflies—A. B. Klots. Houghton Mifflin Company, Boston.
Insect Fact and Folklore—Lucy W. Clausen. The Macmillan Company, New York.
The Insect Guide—Ralph B. Swain. Doubleday & Company, Garden City, New York.
Insects in Their World—SuZan N. Swain. Garden City Books, Garden City, New York.
An Introduction to the Study of Insects—Donald J. Borror and Dwight M. DeLong. Rinehart & Company, Inc., New York.
Larvae of Insects, Part 1: Lepidoptera and Hymenoptera—Alvah Peterson. Edward Brothers Inc., Ann Arbor, Michigan.
The Moth Book—W. J. Holland. Doubleday & Company, Garden City, New York.

Caterpillar of the imperial moth

Channel catfish

CATFISH

The number of species commonly known as catfish is well over a thousand. Although they include some marine fishes, most catfishes inhabit fresh water. Probably the best known catfishes are those of the genus *Ictalurus*.

The tropical fish hobbyist is familiar with many species of tropical catfishes in the genus *Corydoras*. These lively little fishes (about 1½ to 3½ inches long) are used primarily as a scavenger cleanup force for the bottom of the aquarium. The bronze catfish, *Corydoras aneus*, is one of the most popular of the genus. Another group of tropical catfishes, commonly referred to as *suckers*, is used to keep the inside surfaces of aquariums free of algae. One of the most popular of these is the *Plecostomus plecostomus*.

Marine catfishes include the sea catfishes of the family Ariidae. In this group are the gaff-topsail catfish, *Bagre marinus*, and the sea catfish, *Galeichthys felis*.

The well known freshwater catfishes of the genus *Ictalurus* include the bullhead, the channel catfish, the white catfish, and the blue catfish. They all have a sharp, tough spine in their dorsal fins and another in each of their pectoral fins. These spines are connected to poison glands and can inflict an injury as painful as a bee's sting. They also have in common the presence of an adipose dorsal fin set well in back of their dorsal fin (*See under Fish: Topography of a Fish*). An adipose fin is small and fatty and has no rays. The rear third of this fin is a free lobe. In addition, they all have barbels (eight or fewer), which are feelerlike projections from the jaw area. Also, none of them has scales. Like most catfishes they spend the major portion of their time at the bottom and are most active at night. They consume much waste that otherwise cause pollution. —M.R.

Channel Catfish
Other Common Names— Spotted cat, channel cat, speckled catfish, fiddler
Scientific Name—*Ictalurus punctatus*
Family — Ictaluridae (freshwater catfishes)

Order — Cypriniformes
Size — Length, 3 to 4 feet; weight, up to 35 pounds
Range — From Montana to the Lake Champlain region and southward into Mexico and Florida

The channel catfish has a rather slender body, particularly in comparison with the other *Ictalurus* species. Its mouth is comparatively small and its barbels are very long. The dorsal fin is well developed and has the sharp spine that is characteristic of the fish's genus. The anal fin is crescent-shaped and has 24 to 30 rays. The tail fin is deeply forked, which, together with the rounded anal fin is a good way to identify the species.

The fish is silvery gray to light bluish-olive in color. Its sides are lighter than its back and the entire fish is sparsely to thickly covered with circular, dark spots.

Like most catfishes, the channel catfish has a great appetite and eats virtually anything alive or dead. They most commonly eat insects and their larvae, crayfish, snails, small clams, worms, and fishes. They also eat many vegetable materials such as seeds and fruit that drop into the water from nearby trees.

When young, the fishes travel in schools but later go off singly. They seem to prefer areas of swiftly running water. Although most of its activity is nocturnal, the channel catfish is more active in daytime than the others in its genus. It is a delicious food fish, its flesh being firm, white, and full-flavored.

— M.R.

Brown Bullhead
Other Common Names — Northern brown bullhead, speckled bullhead, horned pout
Scientific Name — *Ictalurus nebulosus*
Family — Ictaluridae (freshwater catfishes)
Order — Cypriniformes
Size — Length, 12 inches; weight, 2 to 2½ pounds
Range — From North Dakota into New England, southward to Tennessee and eastern Virginia. Lives in the drainages of the Great Lakes, with the exception of Lake Superior

The brown bullhead's body is more slender than those of the other two common bullheads (the black bullhead and yellow bullhead) but not as slender as that of the channel catfish. Its barbels are long and those that are on the chin are colored gray, black, or black-spotted either along their entire length or only at their bases. The dorsal fin is more rounded than that of the channel catfish and has the characteristic spine of the genus. The spines on each of the pectorals are edged with many small sharp barbs. The anal fin has from 17 to 29 rays and its margin is slightly rounded. The tail fin is not forked, only slightly indented.

The fish's color varies widely from yellowish to black but is usually olive-brown. There are dark green mottlings on the sides, which fade to white or cream color near the belly.

The brown bullhead prefers the quiet waters of lakes or streams. It has a ravenous appetite and eats mostly insects and their larvae, crustaceans, snails, small crayfish, worms, and small fishes. When fall comes the fish becomes sluggish, stops feeding, and may lie quietly in the mud at bottom for weeks. It is a favorite game fish and makes fairly tasty eating.

The brown bullhead can be distinguished from the black bullhead by the barbs on its pectoral spines, its relatively slender body, and the absence of both a light colored bar at the base of its tail fin and black coloration between the rays of its tail fin. It can be distinguished from the yellow bullhead by its dark barbels, the yellow bullhead having whitish chin barbels.

CATKIN

All trees have flowers but those of most of our forest trees are small and inconspicuous. The earliest flowering trees are those whose flowers are borne in catkins. A catkin is a spike bearing flowers without petals. The stamens that produce the pollen and the pistils that contain the ovules are in different catkins. The catkin-bearing trees include willow, poplar, alder, birch, hickory, and oak. Of these the best known is the pussy willow.

WILLOW

Willow trees grow almost universally along water ways. There are many different species, some of which have catkins in which the scales are covered with silvery hairs; these are the "pussy willows." Staminate and pistillate catkins, borne on separate trees, expand before the leaves.

A "Pussy Willow"

BIRCH

Birch trees have staminate and pistillate catkins on the same tree. Conspicuous in winter, the pendulous staminate catkins are ready for the first warm days in March to stimulate development. The pistillate catkins are smaller and develop later than the staminate flowers.

Black Birch

POPLAR

Like the willows, the staminate and pistillate catkins of poplars grow on separate trees and expand early in spring before the leaves. The catkins are grayish, long and drooping, longer and more loosely flowered than those of their cousins, the willows.

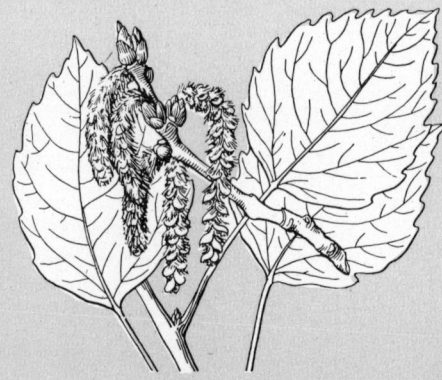

Large-toothed Aspen, a Poplar

ALDER

In swamps and along streams, the common speckled alder may be identified in winter by hanging clusters of purplish-red staminate catkins, with tiny recurved pistillate catkins above them. Clusters of last year's cones persist on the branches. Alders bloom in March.

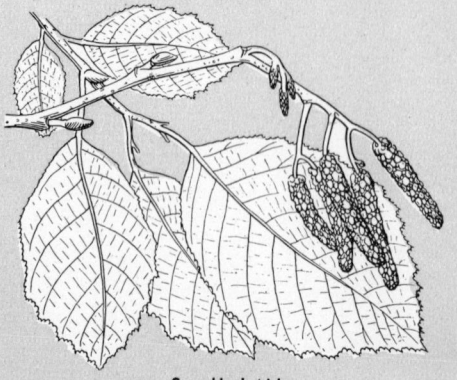

Speckled Alder